GRANT WRITING
FOR AGING SERVICES
AND PROGRAMS

GRANT WRITING
FOR AGING SERVICES AND PROGRAMS

CAROL R. HEGEMAN, MS

WILLIAM C. LANE, PhD

Cover design by The Troy Book Makers
Book design by The Troy Book Makers
Cover image by deosum / 123RF Stock Photo

Printed in the United States of America

The Troy Book Makers • Troy, New York • thetroybookmakers.com

To order additional copies of this title, contact your favorite local bookstore or visit www.tbmbooks.com or www.amazon.com

ISBN: 978-1-61468-378-0

TABLE OF CONTENTS

Preface   vii

Acknowledgments   xiii

PART I
CREATING A GRANT-READY ORGANIZATION   1

CHAPTER 1
Do You Need a Grant or Should You Be Fundraising?   3

CHAPTER 2
Pre-Planning Your Grant Proposal: Modules and Sharing Your Grant Concept to Get Critical Feedback and Support   11

CHAPTER 3
Conceptualizing the Multiple Roles of a Grant Writer for Aging Services   21

PART II
SPECIFIC CONCEPTS FOR GRANTS IN THE FIELD OF AGING   27

CHAPTER 4
Decoding the RFP: Find Out What the Funder Is Really Seeking   29

CHAPTER 5
Three Fictitious Organizations Serving the Aging   45

PART III
WRITING THE PROPOSAL   49

CHAPTER 6
Understanding Proposal Components and Their Linkages   51

CHAPTER 7
How to Create an Effective Abstract and Executive Summary   61

CHAPTER 8
Developing an Effective Needs Assessment   67

CHAPTER 9
How to Create Goals and Objectives 81

CHAPTER 10
Evaluation and Logic Models 89

CHAPTER 11
Building a Logical Work Plan (Methodology) and Timeline 107

CHAPTER 12
Devising a Functional and Accurate Budget 119

CHAPTER 13
Corporate Capability and Qualifications 141

CHAPTER 14
Illustrative Letter of Intent 147

CHAPTER 15
Tricks of the Trade: Reviewing the Completed Proposal 157

PART IV

FINDING AND UNDERSTANDING FUNDING SOURCES AND PROCESSES TO FOLLOW POSTFUNDING 165

CHAPTER 16
Finding and Working With Funders 167

CHAPTER 17
Processes to Follow Postfunding 179

References 195

Glossary *A Grant Writer's Vocabulary* 201

About the Authors 209

PREFACE

If you are in the field of aging and/or new or somewhat new to the grant-writing process, *Grant Writing for Aging Services and Programs* is for you. It is for busy agency and association administrators and managers, faculty, students, volunteers, and others who want a clear step-by-step approach to grant writing.

Why a separate grant-writing book focused on aging? First and foremost, society is aging (Ortman, Selloff, & Hogan, 2014). Therefore, demand on existing aging service entities will not only continue to increase, but will increase at all ends of the aging service spectrum. For example, services for healthy retirees are expanding into the civic engagement and adult learning arenas, while service needs for the oldest-old are also expanding because of the increasing demand for care innovations and cost effectiveness. There will be demand for grants that address these changes, not only from aging service providers, but also from related entities such as hospitals, volunteer organizations, educational entities, and more.

Second, aging gets short shrift in generic books on grant writing. Such books necessarily omit all the specific tips we provide for professionals in the aging service field. In just one example, in Chapter 16 we provide suggestions on how to approach funders who do not typically support grants in aging so that they might well consider your proposal.

However, you do not need to be working in the field of aging to benefit from this book. Here are some examples of other intended readers:

1. Professionals working in allied health fields, such as nursing, physical therapy, occupational therapy, and social work. They will be able to use this book as a guide to develop grants to enhance their aging-related work.

2. State and local advocacy governmental and membership associations working with aging populations who may not have an in-house professional grant writer. They will find targeted assistance in this book.

3. Faculty teaching courses or certificate programs on topics such as gerontology, research methods, administration, and health care. They can add this book to their course.

4. Students interning in an aging service setting. They may be writing a grant as part of their internship experience or as a class assignment.

5. Generic grant writers. Although examples in this book are from the field of aging, the principles of grant writing and the insights are valid in other settings.

6. "Encore career professionals," people who worked in other areas and want to become grant writers as a second career or wish to volunteer on a professional level in the aging sector. They will find this book a way to begin their new work.

7. International aging professionals from outside the US. They will gain insight into an American approach to grant writing for aging services.

Although this book is clearly not geared to people writing complex research grants to funders such as the National Institute of Health, even those kinds of grants writers will find useful tips on grant planning and grant writing.

The authors have a combined 60 years of real-world practical experience in writing grants in aging services plus extensive experience reviewing grants. Many chapters provide a "Sharing What We Have Learned" section based on our varied experience in the entire spectrum of aging services and the reviewing process. Some of these insights are funny, some are sad, but all are illustrative and informative.

We wrote this book to share our successful process for not only "winning a grant," but also for creating a grant that has been carefully crafted so that the organization can manage it successfully. You will see this theme throughout the book, embodied in this question and answer:

> **Question:** What is worse than working for days and nights on a grant proposal your agency really needs and not getting it?
> **Answer:** Getting a grant you are not prepared to manage well.

Third, we are proud of four special features in this book:

1. An entire chapter devoted to a fictitious request for proposal (RFP) in aging and a careful parsing of that RFP. Because of this chapter, you will know exactly how to read an RFP to understand what it expected and what explicit and implicit information is in it.

2. Three fictitious but realistic case studies of aging service providers (a multipurpose senior center, a home care entity and a long term care facility) that wish to respond to the RFP we have parsed in detail. We provide sample sections of a grant proposal for each of these providers in chapters devoted to each section of a typical grant. As a result, you will benefit from examples of how specific sections of a grant should look.

3. Grant writers sometimes find themselves facing ethical dilemmas. For example, should you ask for more money than you really need? We include a discussion of these kinds of ethical dilemmas throughout this book.

4. An unusual organization for a book on grant writing. Our extensive review of other grant-writing books revealed that typically the first third is devoted to finding potential funders, the second third to grant writing itself and the last third to appendices with examples and resources.

By contrast, we made a carefully considered decision to organize this book differently. Our first two parts are devoted to helping readers develop a grant concept that is workable for their organization, assure that organizational staff at all levels is supportive of the proposal and guarantee that the grant concept meets a real need of the organization and its clients. Understanding and implementing this pre-planning process is as important as writing the actual proposal and it is undercovered in most grant-writing books.

Our third part is devoted to the mechanics of grant writing with a strong emphasis on tips for grant writers in aging. We cover how to write the common elements of most grants: the summary, the need statement, goals and objectives, methodology, evaluation, and budget. As noted, there is a separate chapter devoted to each section, each enriched by illustrative examples of grant proposal sections of the three fictitious aging service entities.

Our fourth part covers finding funders and processes to follow after funding.

5. We have chosen a light conversational tone to this book, as if we were talking to you personally. We think that this writing style makes this book especially easy to read and the content easy to absorb.

Last, who are the authors, and why are they especially suited to write this book?

Carol Hegeman, MS, was, for 30+ years, the Director of Research at the Foundation for Long Term Care (FLTC) in Albany, NY. The FLTC is a private, not-for-profit 501(c)(3) research and education organization founded in 1978. In keeping with its mission to improve by research and education the way care for an aging society is delivered, it has a reputation for outstanding research and demonstration projects and for innovative seminars aimed at keeping health care professionals informed of constant changes in the field. The FLTC is affiliated with Leading Age New York (formerly NYAHSA), which represents nearly 600 voluntary long term care providers, from nursing homes to home care agencies.

In that position, she successfully wrote and (equally important) successfully managed over 30 funded demonstration and research grants that benefited elder care providers and the people they serve. Five of these received state or national awards. Carol received the American Society on Aging's 2008 Gloria Cavanaugh Education & Training Award, which honors an individual who has made a significant and long term contribution to training, and education in the field of aging. She has been a frequent reviewer for federal grants.

Carol now operates Hegeman Consulting, a small firm focused primarily on grant-writing training and coaching, and curriculum development and training in aging. Information on Hegeman Consulting can be found by contacting Carol at her LinkedIn profile page, https://www.linkedin.com/in/carol-hegeman-58952821.

William C. Lane, PhD, retired after 25 years as a member of the faculty at State University of New York (SUNY) at Cortland where he was a member of the Department of Sociology/Anthropology and Director of the Center for Aging and Human Services. Since then, he has owned a consulting practice, William Lane Associates, LLC. The practice was first located in the Albany NY area but is now located in Homer, NY. Bill has worked to support aging programs across New York State and the nation. Information on William Lane Associates, LLC, can be found at www.williamlaneassociates.com.

During his years at SUNY Cortland, he both received and managed research grants. He has served as a grant reviewer for numerous agencies, including the Administration on Aging's caregiver research grants. As a consultant he has worked as a grant writer and has managed grants awarded to various organizations, including grants from the New York State Office for the Aging and the State Department of Health.

He is a past president of both the State Society of Aging of New York, from whom he received the Walther M. Beattie, Jr. Award for outstanding service in the field of aging, and Sigma Phi Omega, the National Honor and Professional Society in Gerontology. He is also both a past Treasurer and a Fellow in the Association for Gerontology in Higher Education.

Enjoy this book and may your grant awards be many!

ACKNOWLEDGMENTS

When we began this project several years ago, we had a different audience in mind. Our original idea was to develop a book that was more business oriented, one aimed at consultants and trainers. While we both do consulting and training, after several months we realized that this was not the book we really wanted to write

Why did we change focus? First, aging is the field we know and love: We each have devoted over 30 years to this field. We admire and highly respect the excellent staff that works in aging, students and professors studying aging and other people who advocate and support aging services.

They, not consultants and trainers, are our natural audience. Second, as grant reviewers, we had seen what happens when well-intentioned and over-extended staff of small not-for profits submit grants. These agencies have difficulty competing successfully with the large, well-funded agencies that have a professional grant writing staff or can afford grant consultants. Our hope is that this book will contribute to leveling the playing field for all those small- and medium-sized agencies with great ideas but who only lack the experience to bring them to life.

Therefore, our first acknowledgment is to all the above people. Our professional careers have been enriched because we were lucky enough to work with so many of you.

Second, we would also like to thank our publisher, The Troy Book Makers, of Troy, NY. We are sure we got more attention and support than we would have received from a larger, less personal publisher.

Third, thanks to our copyeditor, Teresa Nolan Barensfeld, of Prof-Edit in Chatham, NY, and our proofreader, Karen Frishkoff, RN and Geriatric Care Manager, of Ghent, NY. However, any errors that you may find in the book are the responsibility of the authors.

Fourth, thanks to those who recommended or endorsed the book.

A special thank you to our spouses, Don Hegeman and Georgia Lane, for three years of patience as we turned our attention to writing, rewriting and rewriting this book when we are sure they wished we were doing something else.

Unnamed in this acknowledgement are all of the specific people, teachers, mentors, colleagues, students, advisory board members and others who contributed so much to our own professional and personal development. Including them individually in this acknowledgement would take up a considerable amount of space in the book. And we know that we would still leave out many and we did not want to risk that.

Carol R. Hegeman and William C. Lane, January 2017.

PART I

CREATING A GRANT-READY
ORGANIZATION

CHAPTER 1

DO YOU NEED A GRANT OR
SHOULD YOU BE FUNDRAISING?

CHAPTER OVERVIEW

In this chapter, you will learn about:

- The similarities and differences between grant writing and fundraising in five areas and the danger of confusing the two income sources

- How to decide whether to write a grant or start a fundraising program

Grant Writing or Fundraising Campaign?

Have you ever had been part of a conversation something like this?

CEO: "Still another state budget cut, and all of our programs are already underfunded."

Board Member 1: "Yup, money is sure tight. Why don't we just apply for a grant to tide us over?"

This is a dangerous approach because "getting a grant" is in no way the same as getting an infusion of cash from a fundraising event or campaign with no restrictions. This chapter will make that difference clear.

Although not everyone in the field completely agrees with the heavily bifurcated distinction we make between grant writing and fundraising (Koenig, 2014), in this book, we choose to emphasize the differences so that there is no confusion about the specific issues in grant writing that do not always apply to fundraising efforts.

Fundraising, cultivating donors, and grant writing are indeed similar in that they are all intended to raise money for an organization and all require careful thought and skillful planning. However, it is critical that agencies new to the grant-writing process understand that income derived from grant funds is different from other kinds of income, because it is quite restricted. Of course, income from a fundraising campaign for a specific purpose shares some, but not all, of the limiting characteristics of grant income.

The following chart shows the distinctions we want to emphasize. Subsequent text provides the details on each line of the chart. You will see the word "usually" a lot in this chart because there are always exceptions. The discussion of each row describes some of these exceptions.

GENERAL FUNDRAISING CAMPAIGNS	GRANT WRITING
Money is usually available for the agency as a whole.	Money is usually targeted for a specific project.
Money is usually fungible.	Money must be spent according to the grant budget.
Effective fundraising increases income.	Grant dollars often are budget neutral, as they are usually intended to support new services that are not in an existing budget.
You do not spend dollars you do not raise.	Grants are a contractual obligation. If a grant is budgeted badly, it can cost the agency money instead of supporting the organization.

First Line in the Chart

GENERAL FUNDRAISING CAMPAIGNS	GRANT WRITING
Money is usually available for the agency as a whole.	Money is usually targeted for a specific project.

Discussion

Unless you have framed your fundraising or your solicitation of donors in terms of one specific goal (building a new addition to your building, for example), when you seek new income through fundraising or donor development, the money raised can be used for any legitimate use of the agency. Annual fund drives, as an example, often support operating costs without any specific limitation. Your agency board may use what monies it receives from these sources for any legitimate purpose it sees fit.

By contrast, a grant award requires limitations on how you spend grant dollars. **After the award is made, the agency cannot decide it no longer wants to do the activities described in the grant and use the award money for something entirely different.** For example, grant funds awarded to train staff in dementia care cannot be diverted to provide funds for a new roof—even if it that roof is leaking right onto the desk of the executive director!

When an organization accepts grant funds, it signs a contract to use the award money to strive to meet the goals described in its application, even if there is a change in agency priorities. Minor changes directly related to the goals and objectives might be allowed, but never assume that they can be made without formal (written) authorization from the funding source.

Second Line in the Chart

GENERAL FUNDRAISING CAMPAIGNS	GRANT WRITING
Money is usually fungible.	Money must be spent according to the grant budget.

Discussion

In grant writing, it is not only the overall scope of the grant that is rarely changed. It is also very hard to change the way you described how you would operate the grant award and spend the dollars awarded to you. You are expected to spend money as the grant budget shows. This limitation goes down to the specific line items in the budget.

Two examples:

1. If you have been awarded a grant for a senior center program on fall prevention and you have stated that you will use grant dollars to offer training on fall prevention in 10 training sites for 150 seniors, you cannot arbitrarily decide that you made an expensive error (whoops, careless me!) and that you will instead reduce your program drastically to operate in only three sites for 45 people. You will have a contract agreeing to perform the project as planned. As a grantee, you cannot assume that a grantor will increase the award because of your miscalculation in costs. It is extremely rare (so much so that neither author is aware of it happening) for this kind of increase to be awarded.

2. You want to move $2,000 in project supply costs into the salary line. You cannot assume that you can simply make this change because you have an unexpected shortfall in your personnel line. A budget modification is required that shows why the grant project (not your organization) requires that change, and it may or may not be granted.

Exceptions

1. Many funders will allow, with prior approval, minor changes in an approved budget. After all, projected numbers are not always right, and funders understand that. For example, if an agency finds that it has under-budgeted its training program costs and needs to train a slightly smaller number of people at fewer site locations, for example, eight sites with 135 people instead of 10 sites with 150 people, it may be possible for a grantor to allow this kind of mod-

est change if accompanied by a logical explanation of the need for the change. The grant award letter often spells out what is and is not allowable. *Never* assume that such a change will be approved without asking, and above all, do not count on it when developing a grant proposal.

2. Some funders allow what are called budget-neutral changes and no-cost extensions:

   a. Budget-neutral changes: Keeping to the same example of the training program on fall prevention, it may be possible to reduce the amount of money in other budget categories to allow the organization to keep the training costs on target. Never assume that this change is possible unless the contract clearly states something like this: "Cost-neutral budget changes between budget lines of no more than 10% are permitted." Without a statement like that, you must make a request to change numbers or activities.

   b. No-cost extensions: Sometimes your agency will not be able to complete the grant on time through no fault of your own. Both of the authors have had the harrowing experience of the very late arrival of project funds, sometimes months late. In this case or for other good reasons, funders may allow for no-cost extensions.

Third Line in the Chart

GENERAL FUNDRAISING CAMPAIGNS	GRANT WRITING
Effective fundraising increases income.	Grant dollars often are budget neutral, as they are usually intended to support new services that are not in an existing budget.

Discussion

Almost all grant proposals are written to accomplish a specific project. It is rare for the grant to be awarded for "general operating expenses," which is why the conversation starting this chapter is unrealistic. Grants are almost never awarded to resolve an existing budget deficit. Rather, they are almost always awarded to provide funds to augment or add new services or programs. Dollars awarded are intended to support those new services, not the existing general operating budget.

Funders usually see the award they make to you as a way of making something new and important happen. They do not see the award as a general gift to the organization, and therefore they expect the award money to support *new* or expanded work.

Exception

Very few foundations or corporate funders offer operating support. If they do, it is usually on a one-time basis. If you run across such a rare opportunity, take advantage of it.

Fourth Line in the Chart

GENERAL FUNDRAISING CAMPAIGNS	GRANT WRITING
You do not spend dollars you do not raise.	Grants are a contractual obligation. If a grant is budgeted badly, it can cost the agency money instead of supporting the organization.

Discussion

You will be expected to strive to meet the goals and objectives you have set. Not doing so is similar to defaulting on a loan in terms of the organization's reputation. While this may seem to be strong language, no agency should submit a proposal it does not think is achievable with the amount of money it has requested or unless it is certain it can find the funds elsewhere.

A badly planned grant, therefore, can be a net loss to the organization. To honor the contract, the agency might need to add its own funds to the grant award rather than endure the public embarrassment of a project that could not be completed or the impression among funders that the agency is unreliable. (Funders do talk with each other!) Simply put, contracts cannot be broken without possible, although unlikely, legal consequences or without taking an embarrassing hit on the agency's reputation.

The paragraph above is intended to scare you. It is written this way to underscore the critical importance of critical grant planning, which you will learn how to do by reading this book.

Let's be clear: This does not mean that every grant must be successful. Some grant projects, even if they are carried out as planned, do not always meet intended goals. Sometimes grants do not work out. Grant makers understand that. In fact, some grants are funded because an agency has a new, untested idea that may or may not work. What is not acceptable is dropping out of a grant midstream because it is costing more than you planned. Dropping out in this manner will give the funder and the general public the lasting impression that the agency is not reliable. Loss of reputation is a social cost that most agencies are not willing to endure, especially if they want more grants in the future.

Now that you have read and absorbed all of the obligations of taking on a grant, you should not then assume that grants are not worth the risk. Without grant money, many excellent projects would never be carried out. A well-crafted grant proposal with adequate input from various members of the leadership staff is more likely to be successful.

If you follow the suggestions in this book, you will be preparing grants that improve lives and services and are also economically viable for your organization. Successful grants are written all the time. You just need to know how to write them. This book will help you do that.

CHAPTER 2

PRE-PLANNING YOUR GRANT PROPOSAL:
MODULES AND SHARING YOUR GRANT CONCEPT
TO GET CRITICAL FEEDBACK AND SUPPORT

CHAPTER OVERVIEW

In this chapter, you will learn about:

- Modules

- How to use a planning abstract to share your formative ideas on a grant proposal

- How and why to gather and use feedback from staff within the agency

- How and why to gather and use external feedback from other stakeholders

- How pre-planning can help you decide whether or not to continue with a grant application

- How to address an ethical dilemma concerning sharing an external critique

Introduction

One of the major premises of this book is that you need to spend considerable time pre-planning your grant concept. We use the term "pre-planning" in this chapter because it provides information on what you have to do before you even begin writing the proposal. This entire chapter is devoted to two components of a pre-planning process: modules and sharing your grant concept.

Modules

We are all busy people and we tend to think of grant writing as something you do when and if a grant opportunity comes along. However, an excellent grant writer is always prepared with some prewritten sections of a proposal that, with strategic modification, can be placed into a proposal, saving time. These sections are modules.

A module is a prewritten, standard piece of a grant proposal that you should work on while you are waiting for the ideal request for proposal (RFP) to come along. The purpose of modules is to free you from as much last-minute writing as possible. Sections of an application that can be drafted in advance (but not finalized) include parts of the budget and the corporate capability sections. Sometimes parts of the needs assessment can be written in advance, for example, the number of elders you serve and their ethnicity and economic status.

A good way to use qualified volunteers and interns is to have them develop these sections in their generic form in advance. For example, they can prepare a needs assessment module for a variety of programs you might want to have. When a grant opportunity in that area appears, you will be well ahead of the game.

While it makes tremendous sense to prewrite sections of a grant, this recommendation comes with a caveat: **Modules must be modified to meet the needs of each particular proposal.**

Let's say you have a generic needs statement in module form, but the particular RFP to which you are responding is focused on increasing the civic engagement of elders. In addition to the basic information on the demographic data of the elders you serve, you would also want to add options for civic engagement that do and do not exist in your area for this particular proposal.

Sharing Your Grant Concept

Once you decide (or someone else in your organization decides for you) that you are going to write a specific grant proposal, you may think that the next thing to do is to read the guidelines and immediately start writing. **This is wrong!**

Why not simply start writing? After all, many of us do tend to write this way, as ideas seem to come to as you write. The answer is that one person writing a proposal without the considered input of other people is likely to result in a grant proposal that is not well conceived and is likely to result in implementation challenges. A winning and effective grant is based on the input of many people and is more comprehensive, workable, and fundable than the work of one person writing alone. Therefore, pre-planning is, above all, getting input from others.

Getting this useful input is far more than tapping a busy co-worker on the shoulder and asking, "What do you think?" You will tend to get either a "Sure, whatever" or "What? Don't even think of sticking me with more work" kind of response. If you want considered and honest input that reflects the needs of the people you serve, you have to make it easy for colleagues to reflect on your early grant concept and to share their thoughts in a meaningful way. You will also want feedback from the people who will benefit from the grant. Here is how to do that in four steps.

Step 1: Create a planning abstract (short summary) of your proposal.
Keep in mind that the planning abstract you develop will change dramatically over time as you work on it and incorporate feedback from others. Using an art metaphor, consider it a scribbled sketch done in pencil that can be erased rather than a finished work ready for hanging.

It should only be a few paragraphs (or even one) and never more than one page. While the content will vary with the type of the grant, a good planning abstract will contain your first (and perhaps even inaccurate) thoughts on topics such as the following:

- Why does your community need this grant?
- What will the grant accomplish (grant goals and objectives)?
- How will your agency execute this grant?

It is likely that you will not know enough at this early planning stage to be able to complete these paragraphs fully. That is fine. You will find that writing an abstract focuses your thoughts. The box below contains a sample planning abstract that a grant writer in aging services might construct.

SAMPLE PLANNING ABSTRACT

We seek funds to increase the community's awareness of elder abuse issues and solutions to reduce them, because countywide data show that this kind of abuse is increasing each year. (*Note to self: get data later.*) In addition, our caseworkers are seeing increased instances of unreported numbers of emotional, physical, and financial abuse. (*Caseworkers—can you show me the numbers?*)

We will work with community libraries, places of worship, senior housing, and _____ (*ideas here*) to offer a series of 25 free seminars to reach an estimated 500 people in East County. (*Ideas please: How will we recruit participants? Do we want professional staff as well as elders themselves? Does our target audience consist of members of the community, agency staff, or both?*)

Law students will conduct training. (*Retired attorneys as well? Other? Perhaps staff of the county office for the aging? How will we gain cooperation of law schools and Area Agencies on Aging [AAAs], and what percentage of grant funds must be delivered to them? What challenges and assets do you see for us if we submit this proposal?*)

As you can see, this planning abstract is not complete, which is as it should be. The purpose of the blanks and questions is to encourage the people with whom you share it to feel free to speak up and share ideas. If you provide a complete, polished document, there is a tendency for people not to comment, thinking it is already cast in stone.

Step 2: Use your planning abstract as a way to reach out to people within your organization to get feedback on the concept.
The purposes for conducting this internal discussion of the abstract within the organization are:

- To get wisdom from multiple stakeholders.

- To build support and commitment among staff and prevent staff resistance later. This is a critical step: Staff members who are excluded from the discussion of a grant concept may later resent the grant and the time they need to spend working on it.

- To learn what already exists and therefore not worth funding. Better to know this now than later.

- To find out any previous history with similar projects or an existing competing project, and if the experience was negative, to see if the concept can be reworked to make it successful.

- To hear the concerns and ideas of the older persons and their families who will benefit from the program.

This last bullet merits special attention. If you expect to have a project with great outcomes, you need to know exactly how to serve your clients. Only by talking directly with them will you get their perspective. For example, if you are writing a grant to serve family caregivers, you need to speak with more than one kind of family caregivers, as shown in the box below.

> ### SHARING WHAT WE HAVE LEARNED
>
> One of us wrote and managed a grant to provide support for family caregivers. In preparation for the writing the grant, the agency team conducted two focus groups, one with children who were caregiving for their parents and the other with spouses who were caregivers. The fo-

> cus groups revealed that while both groups shared some similar needs, each had unique problems and concerns. As a result, the team was able to craft the proposal to meet the overlapping needs of both groups and address the specific needs of each group. Without this input into the project design, the project would have been far less successful.

Invite input from the fiscal department at as well. Your financial staff may rightly say that they cannot discuss numbers without much more detailed information and that you should approach them later. Your response should be that you are not seeking specific costs at this point, but rather it is their expertise in identifying cost centers that you need to consider.

One example: In our early days of grant writing, one of us planned a project in which volunteers would drive homebound seniors to supermarkets. We had not considered the significant expense of liability insurance for the drivers. It was only the early input of a fiscal officer that resulted in the inclusion of this cost in the project budget.

Sometimes after talking with all levels of staff, volunteers, and recipients, you will experience consistent negative feedback about the grant concept. Despite your best efforts and fervent belief that the grant project would be exceptional and important, the wisest thing to do is to give it a pass. Every grant project needs cheerleaders in the organization and community, and if you cannot find them, it is almost always best, at this early point, to move on to a different project.

Step 3: Use your planning abstract as a way to reach out to appropriate stakeholders in your community to get feedback on your grant concept. There are several reasons for this outreach step. First, other aging service providers may feel competition from your new grant proposal. If you are offering a duplicative service, they would be absolutely right! It is never wise to apply for grant funds to compete head-on with another provider of service when there is no established need for more services. Of course, get the prior approval of your executive director before sharing ideas on behalf of your agency.

A planning discussion with similar neighboring entities can help you to ensure that there is no direct competition or to plan a niche area for your proposal that does not directly compete with other entities and may indeed enhance them. If you find that other agencies are already involved, you may be able to find a modest way to include the other agencies in the grant. For example, after you have finished implementing and evaluating a project, include grant funds to train other agencies in your project. There is a lot of practical wisdom in the community, and reaching out to others to get their input may yield wonderful ideas for your proposal.

Finally, funders often like proposals that involve more than one agency in a given community. By working with another entity, you might not only build a better proposal to serve your community but also impress the potential funder favorably.

SHARING WHAT WE HAVE LEARNED

One of us was writing a training grant for a not-for-profit provider. The governmental funder was (unusually) allowing for-profit entities to compete for funding. The author knew that a for-profit competitor was also preparing a similar proposal and therefore sought permission from the CEO to work with this competitor on the proposal. Because there was long-standing competition between the two entities, the CEO rejected the idea of collaboration.

Several months later, the proposals of both agencies were rejected. The funder pointedly wrote that it gave the award to another area in the state where there was a collaborative proposal involving all sectors in the training. *Lesson learned: When appropriate, collaborate rather than compete.*

Ethical Dilemma 1: Will conducting an external critique alert your competitors to the grant opportunity you have found, and will they then steal your idea and submit a competing grant? This is one of the very tough judgment calls you will have to face, and there is no perfect answer.

There may be a few cases where the decision is relatively easy. Let's say, for example, that one of your board members has a brother who has just joined a new foundation supporting aging services and has told you that they will be quietly awarding grants in their first year and that your agency should apply. It is unlikely that other agencies in the community know about this opportunity. The dollar award is truly not amenable to sharing, as the dollars are enough only to benefit your own clients. This is one case where you might not feel the need to share information since the funder clearly does not want a large number of grant applications and the award is not big enough to share in any case.

When faced with this kind of dilemma, (one in which you run a risk of creating competitors for the same funding) consider these questions:

1. Would this particular grant work better if more than one agency were engaged in it? Or, is it best run by one agency?

2. Is there enough money to support a project that runs in more than one agency?

3. Is the funder looking for a new idea that needs testing (therefore making it appropriate for one agency to apply) or is it seeking to serve as many people as possible?

4. Are the two or more collaborating agencies likely to be able to work together, sharing the work as well as the grant dollars?

The judgment call will still be tough, but you will have thought it through logically.

Step 4: Ask yourself these questions to help you decide whether your grant concept is viable or not.

1. What was the input from the internal and external discussion of your abstract? If the preponderance of feedback is negative after considerable discussion and considered efforts to make it more appealing, it almost always makes sense to move on to something else and not write a grant that is not wanted.

2. Do we know how to execute this project well? Sometimes an appealing proposal requires expertise you do not have. In some cases, it will be possible to hire someone with the requisite expertise and add capacity that way. In some cases, that will not be the case.

3. A good internal and external review will help you decide whether your organization can grow into the grant or whether you are overreaching. The favorite mantra of this book is appropriate here: The only thing worse than not getting a grant you're worked hard on is getting a grant you cannot manage well.

4. Do we have the expertise to both write the proposal now and manage it well later? Sometimes the stars align against you. The perfect person to write the grant may be off on parental leave, and no one else can take it on. Or, the perfect person to manage it is retiring the same month the grant will start. Depending on your organization, you may or may not be able to overcome these challenges. It might make more sense to pass on a great grant opportunity than to take on more than you can handle.

5. If you happen to have a funder in mind already (you may not at this early stage), is the project congruent with the goals of the funder without engaging in wishful thinking?

6. Is the amount of the potential grant award enough to cover the costs of the project, including direct costs as well as other staff expenses? This question may not be completely answerable until much more work is done on the grant proposal, but sometimes the answer becomes obvious early on. For example, the comments on the draft abstract may make it resoundingly clear that a much

larger budget is needed than the grant funds that are available. This fact may not have been apparent before you began an internal and external review.

7. Have you considered the opportunity cost of writing this particular proposal? Opportunity cost is a useful concept when deciding whether or not to pursue a particular grant proposal. Opportunity cost is generally defined as "the benefit that could have been gained from an alternative use of the same resource" (see the *Collins English Dictionary—Complete & Unabridged, 2012 Digital Edition*, http://www.collinsdictionary.com/dictionary/english/opportunity-cost). What does this mean for an aging service provider? If you are spending precious time on a grant proposal that is not of real importance to your agency, you may not have the time to do another proposal that will better meet the needs of the older people you serve.

In summary, pre-planning by creating modules is a wonderful time-saving tool that you should use before you have a grant opportunity in your sight. In addition, pre-planning with your staff, your clients, and community stakeholders will improve the design of your proposal and improve your chances of success.

CHAPTER 3

CONCEPTUALIZING THE MULTIPLE ROLES OF A GRANT WRITER FOR AGING SERVICES

CHAPTER OVERVIEW

In this chapter, you will learn about the multiple roles of an effective grant writer including:

- Grant application guru, a stickler for detail who pays close (some might say obsessive) attention to the guidelines for the proposal

- Marketer (you are selling a concept to a funder who is reading many other proposals)

- Management professional (or someone who can access advice on management issues in the organization)

- Guardian of the agency's short-term *and* long-term needs

- Sustainability watchdog

Introduction

Most aging service organizations are small entities that often do not have their own grant writers. Like most not-for-profits and governmental entities, they are typically operating with a short complement of overworked staff. As a result, there is a tendency to write a proposal in haste without enough attention to its impact on the agency or the way it will appear to the reviewer, and then naively hope it will all work out well in the end. This is not a recipe for success.

Writing a successful proposal demands that grant writers understand, foster, and complete their multiple roles, as described next.

Role 1: Grant Application Guru

Although this topic will be discussed in greater detail in Chapter 4, we have included it in this chapter because it is a critical conceptual role of the grant writer. New grant writers tend to start working on a proposal without careful scrutiny of what is required. Never just start on Section 1 and work your way down! This approach is rather like starting to cook a recipe without checking that you have all of the ingredients or without realizing that you do not fully understand the directions. This lack of attention to the requirements can result in both a mismatch with funder needs and fatal flaws in the application.

By mismatch, we don't only mean a gross mismatch in which an applicant requests funds for a new furnace when the request for proposal (RFP) is designed specifically for arts programming. We also mean the subtler mismatches that occur when the title of the proposal matches the general need of the applicant, but the grant application details make it clear that only one specific type of program is of interest, and the grant proposal does not address that specific interest.

Therefore, the application guru also studies the proposal to learn answers to this set of questions:

Question 1: What does the funder really want?

The answer to what the funder wants often cannot be discerned by the title of the RFP or even by a cursory read. For example, an RFP title may be "Bringing the Arts to All People." This title may seem perfect for bringing arts to a nursing home. However, a closer review of the proposal makes it clear that the funder is interested only in bringing professional art programs to performance spaces in underserved areas. Art therapy programs, therefore, may not be a good fit despite the title.

Question 2: What are the mechanics of writing the proposal?

Are you sure of the due date, page length, font restrictions, and so forth? Is there a letter of intent required and, if so, when is it due? The last thing you want is to realize that you have these pieces of critical information wrong at the last minute, or worse, after the grant has been submitted. Each of us has seen truly excellent proposals worthy of full funding get rejected because the writer exceeded the page limit. Details count.

Question 3: What else is needed besides the narrative and budget?

We discuss boilerplate (required standard forms and information) in Chapter 6. While it may seem obsessive to be searching for all of these forms and signed documents early in the writing process, it is critical. Murphy's Law applies to grant writing in many ways. You do not want to realize that your accountant, the only one who knows the numbers for the combination lock on the file cabinet file holding the last fiscal audit, is on a cruise to Antarctica the week the proposal is due.

Role 2: Marketer

Effective grant writers must consider not only the needs of their clients and their agency but also the expectations of the funder. Every proposal that the grant reviewer will read will have information on the needs of the clients and the agency. Often the needs of other agencies are the same as yours. Therefore, you need to think about how to market your proposal so that it stands out among others. Here are two questions to help you understand marketing goals:

- Does your proposal meet the guidelines of the grant extraordinarily well?
- Is there anything unique or highly appropriate in this proposal?

It is the task of the grant writer to ensure that the answer to these two questions is "yes" and that these answers are clear to the reviewer. This is far more the just stating your needs.

Some grant-writing books stress that you need to talk about the people who will benefit rather than providing data only. Of course, if you have room, a compelling anecdote of who will benefit is terrific and a great tool in your marketing arsenal. However, be careful not to overdo stories at the expense of impressive empirical information about the importance of the project.

In addition, the marketing role includes making it easy for the reviewer to follow your ideas and concepts. No matter how objective a reviewer tries to be, it is human nature to prefer a proposal that is easy to follow over one that has information scattered all over the place and does not present information in the same order as the RFP. Further, reviewers get distracted by spelling and grammatical errors. If they are mentally correcting your work, they may be missing out on your content.

Role 3: Management Professional

The grant writer must work in concert with executive staff to assure the potential funder that the agency

1. Is fully capable of carrying out these plans.

2. Has a cost-effective plan.

3. Provides documented reasons to believe the project will succeed.

4. Includes plans for the project to be sustained after funding ends (if applicable).

A lack of clarity in these areas is a red flag for reviewers. In fact, it is often part of criteria for selection. Therefore, managerial and fiscal acumen and the ability to convey this acumen to the funder must be part of the arsenal of the effective grant writer. *You* may know that your agency excels, but if the reviewer does not see evidence of this, all the ability in the world will not matter.

And what if you, the grant writer, do not know about the organization's management capability? That is not an uncommon situation, especially if you are new to the agency or are an outside consultant. When it occurs, it is imperative for the grant writer to insist on enough meetings early in the process so that executive staff in the agency can provide the needed management and fiscal information that must be incorporated into the proposal.

The specific information needed will, of course, depend on the nature of the grant proposal. Obviously, a small grant to set up a speaker series will have modest amount of management details, while a grant to set up a new line of service in the aging service area will be replete with information of this kind.

This kind of coordination with management and fiscal staff cannot be left to the last moment. It is common to call in fiscal staff to draw up the final budget after the entire narrative is complete. However, as stated in earlier chapters, an early review of the grant concept by fiscal and management staff will alert the grant writer to cost centers that need to be incorporated not only into the budget but also into the narrative.

Role 4: Guardian of the Agency's Short-Term and Long-Term Needs

Of course, the grant writer is not usually the CEO who has the responsibility for making decisions about the agency's needs and carrying out the priorities of the board of directors. The grant writer, however, should have a role in helping the CEO consider whether the grant is congruent with the vision of the organization.

People at all levels in an organization can get temporarily blinded to the future when faced with the possible infusion of immediate cash that a grant can provide. A good grant writer or CEO will at least raise the question of whether pursuing a specific grant is congruent with the strategic plan or not. Put another way, would the time and effort on a proposed grant be better used in finding funding for a more core mission? (See the concept of opportunity cost discussed in Chapter 2.)

This economic consideration does not—by any means—suggest that small quality-of-life grants that enrich the care or services of elders must be bypassed in favor of more major ones. Of course not: Everyone in the aging service sector should be considering grants, even modest, that enrich lives. This is an ongoing mission of this sector. What it does mean is that grants that do not in some logical way support the current and future mission may not be a logical choice, even though an organization might be eligible to get grant funding.

Role 5: Sustainability Watchdog

For projects that plan to continue after funding, an increasing number of grant funders pose this pointed question: "How will the organization keep the project going after the fundraising period ends?" Alas, many grant writers skirt this question with answers like, "We will seek alternative funders." This is an insufficient answer for two major reasons: (1) it will not satisfy the funder since these alternative funders are unnamed, and you are avoiding the question of what will happen after the next funding stream is gone, and (2) you will be letting clients down if a service available through a grant is suddenly no longer available. Part of a good marketing plan and a good management plan is to think through more substantive answers.

PART II

SPECIFIC CONCEPTS FOR
GRANTS IN THE FIELD OF AGING

CHAPTER 4

··

DECODING THE RFP: FIND OUT WHAT
THE FUNDER IS REALLY SEEKING

CHAPTER OVERVIEW

In this chapter, you will learn about:

- Reading a request for proposal (RFP) critically so you can discern the interests and values (sometimes not clearly stated) of the potential funder.

- Let's be clear: This chapter does not tell you how to complete an RFP. What you are learning here is how to read an RFP so you will be ready to respond to a variety of both stated and implicit elements.

Introduction

We know of no governmental entity, foundation, or corporation that seeks to make its request for proposal (RFP) difficult or confusing. We are sure that their goal is just the opposite. Yet, many grant writers find RFPs very difficult to follow. Therefore, the goal of this chapter is to enable readers to understand RFPs and learn how to find implicit hints on what the funder values.

We start with a fictitious RFP as a teaching tool. Why not an RFP from a real foundation? There are three reasons:

1. No one RFP we found had all the elements we wanted to cover, and we thought having multiple RFPs would create a chapter that would be too long and too daunting.

2. By developing a fictitious RFP, we were able to include the typical components of all kinds of funders (governmental, foundations, and corporate).

3. We wanted to include many things a novice grant writer might miss. By creating this RFP, we were able to include many more hidden pieces of information than you would normally find in any one proposal. Happily, we have never seen a real RFP with so much hard-to-find information. The fictitious RFP we provide was designed as a teaching tool rather than as an example of a typical RFP.

Note: Not every application has all of the sections included in this one. We made a deliberate decision to include as many sections as possible to familiarize readers with what they might find. Conversely, a funder may add sections to its RFP that have not been included in this chapter.

Just for fun—can you figure out how we came up with the name of this hypothetical foundation and the name of the hypothetical county in which it operates? (Answers are at the end of this chapter.) And now, here is the RFP from the fictitious Nale Foundation.

The RFP of the Nale Foundation

Our mission: The overall mission of the Nale Foundation is to improve the lives of people in Hengema County. The foundation has a particular interest in programs that improve literacy, care for the aged, and the environment, but will consider other projects that meet a pressing community need.

Who is eligible for a grant? Applicants must (a) possess proof of not-for-profit status, (b) have been in existence for at least 3 years, and (c) operate in Hengema County.

Additional restrictions: We do not (a) fund religious or political activities of any kind or (b) provide funding for major capital campaigns, fundraising events, or any onetime event.

Other requirements: We require that there be a credible plan to keep the project operational after the funding period ends. Funding may be awarded for 1–2 years. Any second-year funding is contingent on progress made in Year 1.

Funding guidelines for this year: This year we are seeking to fund new programs that provide services and support for the older adults in our community. We will consider a broad range of applications, including but not limited to:

1. Increasing civic engagement of retirees and other older adults

2. Enhancing the ability of elders with disabilities to live at home

3. Improving quality of care in assisted living facilities and nursing homes

4. Supporting renovation grants related to elder care services

Proposals must be submitted on line no later than midnight June 30, ___. Funding decisions will be announced in October ____, and grants may commence on January 1, ____. (Fill in the blank for the years you are planning for).

Funding: For applications for the first three categories above, the funding range for grant awards this year is $8,000 to $25,000 for the entire life of the project. For the last category (renovation grants), awards for the entire life of the project can range from $100,000 to $200,000, with a minimum 25% cash match.

Required Sections for This Grant

Executive Summary (300 words maximum): Provide an overview of your project. Include the project name, why the project is needed, the goals of the project, and how you will accomplish the project goals. Provide your start and end dates, as well as the dollar amount of your grant request.

Statement of Need (1,000 words maximum): Tell us why this project is needed in Hengema County. Provide data that document the need. How are you going to address this need? Are there organizations or programs in your community that are successfully addressing the same need? If there are, how will you work together?

Goals and Objectives (300 words maximum): Provide one overarching goal and up to five measurable objectives. Provide specific data on the numbers served and dosage of intervention(s) if applicable. Complete the Number Rubric at the end of this application.

Needs Assessment and Rationale (1,000 words maximum): Explain why your project is a solution to the problems you have described. Why did you decide on this particular approach over other options?

Work Plan (1,500 words maximum): Explain in detail how you will run your project. Include a timeline as an attachment (not in the text of this section).

Evaluation (500 words): What is your process for evaluating success in achieving your organization's (or your program's) goals?

Organizational Capability Statement (750 words): In addition to a description of your agency and staff, include (a) how your organization will sustain the project after the funding period ends and (b) experience with managing grant projects.

Line-Item Budget (one page): You can use your own format for the line-item budget. Create a line for in-kind and cash matching funds. Complete a separate section for each year.

Budget Narrative (1,000 words): Explain your costs and how they were derived. Provide a unit cost for services. Include sources for in-kind and matching funds and the extent to which they are assured.

Number Rubric (Include in Attachments):

1. Number to be served, engaged, or affected by project: ____
2. Percent ages 65 or older: ____
3. Percent of your target population that is an ethnic minority: ____
4. Percent of target population that is low income: ____
5. Add other characteristics of target population, if applicable:

Attachments: The following materials must be emailed to the Nale Foundation programofficer@Nalefoundation.org *after* you have received an application number, which will be included with a confirmation of your online submission. They must be received by July 1, ___. (You will receive an automatic confirmation when your proposal is submitted.)

1. Timeline

2. Number rubric

3. A logic model (not required for renovation grants)

4. Resumes for project director and any other key project staff

5. Letters of support (if appropriate)

6. Letters of commitment from collaborators (if applicable)

7. List of current board members with affiliations

8. Internal Revenue Service (IRS) letter documenting 501(c)(3) status or other evidence of federal nonprofit status

9. Most recent financial audit (preferred) or IRS Form 990

Selection Process

There is a three-tiered review: (1) Staff will review the proposal to see if all of the required conditions and information have been met. Incomplete proposals or proposals not meeting the goals of the RFP will be rejected at this point. (2) Staff and outside reviewers will critique proposals and recommend projects to the board of directors. (3) The board of directors will make the final decision on funding.

The review team of staff and outside reviewers will use the following criteria in its review as well as a review of the applicant's responsiveness to each section in the narrative:

1. The program includes a convincing plan to ensure program continuation after funding ends. (pass/fail)

2. The program provides a needed new service for the elderly population of Hengema County. (30 points)

3. The applicant's program plan is clear, detailed, and realistic. (20 points)

4. The evaluation plan uses a quasi-experimental design and is designed appropriately for the project. (10 points)

5. The applicant has stated the extent to which the program is likely to reduce the overall costs of delivering direct services to the aging. (5 points, not applicable to renovation grants)

6. The logic model is clear, convincing, and complete and is congruent with the narrative. (5 points)

7. The applicant entity has provided compelling evidence that it and its staff have the background and capacity to run the proposed project successfully. (20 points)

8. The budget is reasonable. The budget narrative is clear and includes information on the unit cost per participant. (10 points)

Let's begin parsing this proposal, using a question, answer, and tips approach. We suggest that when starting your own proposal, you pose each of these seven questions to yourself and be sure that you know the answers and have considered the tips before writing. As a self-test, write down your answers to these questions and compare them with the answers we have provided.

Question 1: When is this proposal due, and in what format must it be submitted?

Answer: This proposal is due on June 30 and is accepted only online. Each section has a specific word limit. Additional forms need to be submitted after the narrative has been submitted.

Tips:

1. For an online submission, try entering some mock text in the boxes to be sure you are able to do so and that the word or character count of the RFP matches the word or character count on the computer you will be using. Sad fact: They often don't, and you

may find that your word count of 250 comes up on the application form as 280. For example, on some online applications "word count" actually means a "words and spaces" count. Forewarned is forearmed: Last-minute technical glitches may not only be extremely frustrating, but they can also cause you to miss a deadline or submit a quickly revised proposal with errors.

2. Once you know there is good congruence with computers and word or character counts, write your drafts on your own computer and save them before placing them online. That way, you will always have an extra copy.

3. If the funder requires a mailed submission rather than an on-line one, be sure you know whether the deadline means must be "mailed by" (with the postmark serving as proof of receipt) or "received by." Even if you use express mail, the difference can be crucial.

4. Consider your actual deadline to be at least two days before the actual due date. Tell people who are completing sections for you that the due date to get text to you is five days or more before the actual due date. These dates are actually right—you need those days to review, enter text, and handle those last-minute emergencies that seem always to occur.

Question 2: Does the foundation impose any specific limitations?
Answer: Yes. First, you have to (a) be a not-for-profit entity, (b) have been in existence for at least three years, and (c) operate in Hengema County. Second, the foundation will not fund religious or political activities of any kind, major capital campaigns, fundraising events, or any onetime event. Third, there must be a "credible" plan for sustainability after the project ends.

Note that the third point is considered so important by the Nale Foundation that in the selection criteria this element is rated "pass/fail." This means that without a credible plan for sustainability, your application will be rejected outright no matter how good it is in other areas. Therefore, having a sustainability plan is just as critical as writing a strong proposal. Note that the sustainability discussion is not needed for renovation grants.

It is not enough just to look at bulleted items. Reread the first sentence in "Funding guidelines for this year" (above). In that section, the foundation specifies that it wants to fund "new" programs. This is an important piece of information. This requirement would seem to mean that expansion of an existing program is not appropriate. If we were responding to this proposal, we would certainly ask in advance about the specific definition of "new." It may or may not mean: (a) a program completely new to the county; (b) a program new to the area of the applicant, but available in other parts of the county; or (c) a new component to an existing program.

Tips:

1. Be sure that you have read through any application for limitations and be sure that they do not apply to your organization. Look everywhere in the RFP, not just in the specific guidelines for writing the narrative.

2. Always consider if there are legitimate ways around restricting limitations. For example, if your organization has only been operating for 1 year instead of the required 3 years, or if you are governmentally funded, a possibility (note that the operant word here is *possibility*) is to find an agency that meets all the criteria and may be willing to be the lead partner in the proposal and contract with you to provide some services in your area of expertise. The lead partner is the agency that applies for and manages the grant.

3. The option in Tip #2 means less money for you, but in some cases it might work. This partner would be the lead agency, and you would have to discuss whether such an option is acceptable with the Nale Foundation. Never assume variations like this are possible—always check with foundation staff.

4. For governmental entities that do not have 501(c)(3) status, consider forming a not-for-profit subsidiary for an opportunity for

the next round of funding. This is a long-term solution, as the legal and political work involved takes time, but it opens access to many types of grants you could not otherwise get. The Nale Foundation criterion to limit funding to not-for-profits is common to almost all foundation grants.

Question 3: What kind of projects does the funder seek? Is the funder specific or open-ended?

Answer: This funder provides specific examples of what it seeks:

1. Increasing civic engagement of retirees and other older adults

2. Enhancing the ability of elders with disabilities to live at home

3. Improving quality of care in assisted living facilities and nursing homes

4. Supporting renovation grants related to elder care services

Tips: The funder is also somewhat open-ended, as it states that will consider other projects that seek "to support new programs that fund services and provide for the older adults in our community."

In another example of the need for careful reading, note that senior housing is not mentioned specifically in the listing of what it seeks. However, it would seem to be included under the open-ended category of "enhancing the ability of elders with disabilities to live at home," but that is only a guess. It would be prudent to clarify if you are a housing entity.

Question 4: Are there any unusual terms, requests, or comments in the grant narrative?

Answer: Especially if you are new to grant writing or you are responding to an RFP in an area you do not know well, you may come across wordings or phrases that are not clear to you. Be sure to ask colleagues or ask someone with grant-writing experience to explain them to you, or research such terms on your own. Failing that, you should try to contact the funder to determine the precise meaning and intent. See the following box.

SHARING WHAT WE HAVE LEARNED

Carol Hegeman uses the fictitious Nale Foundation RFP when conducting grant-writing training. Never do what one participant in a grant-writing workshop did: When he read a phrase he did not fully understand in this fictitious RFP, he just guessed. He misinterpreted civic engagement to mean participation in the voting process only, and therefore he eliminated this category from consideration for his grant proposal. However, his agency was eager to start a program in which seniors would tutor youth, which is considered civic engagement. Luckily, this was an educational workshop and not a real consideration of a proposal. What a waste that would have been!

Another phrase in this proposal is likely to confuse someone unfamiliar with research terminology: The phrase "dosage of intervention" appears in the "Goals and Objectives" section. If your understanding of the term "dosage" is the amount of medication you should take, this phrase may make no sense and you may be tempted simply to ignore it. As a grant writer, you do not have the luxury of ignoring what you do not understand or simply making a good guess. You need to know. In this case, dosage means how for how long and for what time period a participant will be engaged with the intervention. For example, in a training grant you would have to write a phrase such as "each participant would have __ sessions for __ minutes two times a week over a __-week period."

As we wrote this proposal, we deliberately added some elements that are not always part of the average RFP:

1. The "Statement of Need" component of the RFP asks, "Are there organizations or programs in your community that are successfully addressing the same need?" and "If there are, how will

you work together?" These are great questions and we wish that they were asked more often.

However, for the grant writer, they demand extra work that cannot be put off until the end of the project. Answering this question is time consuming and requires a priori collaboration, so it must be worked on immediately.

In other words, a careful review of the RFP should help you design your work flow. As noted earlier, never assume that you start on Section 1 and just work your way down!

2. The "Needs Assessment and Rationale" section asks, "Why did you decide on this particular approach over other options?" You will be required to find, consider, and report on evaluations of other options, not just state what you are going to do.

Tip: Even if another RFP does not explicitly ask these questions, consider providing answers to them in your proposal. This will show the reviewer how carefully you have been thinking about the project.

Question 5: Are there any surprises in the "Number Rubric" section?
Answer: Yes! This is the *only* place in the entire RFP in which there are questions related to the number of clients who are culturally diverse or low income. While this information is not repeated anywhere else in the application, a savvy grant writer would do well to devote at least some text in the narrative to these issues. Since it is there, it is probably an unstated value of the funder. A savvy grant writer looks for such "unstated values" and addresses them as well as the ones that are clearly stated.

Tip: It is important to pay attention to the content of forms or separate documents. There may be hints in them as to what the funder considers important that are not stated elsewhere.

Question 6: What are the criteria for judging the proposal? Was there information in the criteria section that was not elsewhere in the narrative?

Answers: First, unlike some funders who do not share this information and leave you to infer from other text how the proposal might be graded, the Nale Foundation clearly describes how the application will be judged and the point value for each question. (See the "Selection Process" section in this chapter.)

This section contains three items that are easy to miss or misunderstand:

1. It may be tempting to think that since one area is worth only 5 points, you can put little effort into it. As grant reviewers, we know that successful proposals and unsuccessful proposals may differ only in a 0.2% overall ranking. Pay attention to everything.

2. There are significant surprises in the criteria. Since having a plan to continue the project after funding ends is a pass/fail criterion, it is essential that you write convincingly in this area about a compelling plan for sustainability.

3. It is only in this section (and not in the directions for completing the narrative) that you learn the following: (a) the evaluation must be in a quasi-experimental design (Chapter 10 will explain this term); (b) you need to show that the project is likely to reduce the cost of providing services; and (c) your description of the qualifications of key staff should relate to work on the project; that is, you cannot simply cut and paste sections of someone's resume. It needs to be tailored to the proposal.

The amount of information in the criteria but not in the general guidelines does not (thankfully) occur often, but we have seen it occur in the RFPs of foundations and governmental entities. Read the entire proposal before you start writing! Missing the information in the criteria listed in the "Selection Process" section because you focused on the narrative would probably cost you the grant.

Tips:

1. Make it easy for the reviewer to see how well your application matches the criteria. When possible, echo the wording of the criteria. For example, for the first bullet on program continuation,

you might start a paragraph with "To ensure that our program will continue after funding ends, we will. . . ." You might use this pattern with each of the criteria as appropriate.

2. We cannot overstate how important it is to consider the funding criteria as well as the guidelines as you craft your proposal. Integrate both sections into your narrative.

Question 7: Did you notice the list of required attachments and the unusual procedure for submitting them separately from the narrative?
Answer: Yes, there are eight required attachments, and they must be mailed *after* the narrative has been emailed and applicants have received a tracking number.

 Tips:

1. Any two-part application process doubles the chance for something to go awry. When there are separate activities, be sure the second part is not omitted. There is a natural celebratory reaction when a narrative is emailed or mailed traditionally and an equally natural tendency to forget about any second parts. This tendency is even worse when the dues dates are different. Therefore, it is prudent not only to mark the second deadline in your calendar but also to have a different person in charge of sending the second component.

2. Do not wait until the due date to look for all of the required attachments even if you are sure you know where they are. Unless your office is very different from the ones we worked in, papers have a way of going missing. This applies as well to forms kept online, especially if they are on someone else's computer. In theory, documents should not disappear online, but somehow they do or a file gets corrupted.

Generic Tips on Contacting the Funder for Information or Clarification About the RFP
We suggested contacting the funder several times in this chapter. How-

ever, it is not always easy or appropriate to do so. It is also easy to contact them badly. Here are some general suggestions, but ultimately you must rely on your own good judgment.

If you are welcomed to do so (e.g., the RFP give you specific persons to call for specific types of questions), go ahead and make your contact. However, with your call, remember that you are providing an important first impression of your organization. Therefore:

1. Use your call or email carefully to provide a positive image of your organization. Be organized and succinct. Be able to explain your project in a few sentences. This is sometimes called an "elevator speech," a description you could give to a passenger in an elevator for the 60 or so seconds you are together. Practice saying these few sentences in advance.

2. Do not argue or whine. You are fact-finding and not trying to change the scope of the RFP. Neither you nor the program officer can do that.

3. If there is no information on whether or not you can contact the funder (check the web page as well as the RFP), you might start by emailing and asking if it is appropriate for you to request an appointment to discuss questions about the proposal.

4. If there is clear wording that no calls or emails are wanted, don't call. Consider how a funder might think: "If they cannot follow directions on the RFP, why would we think that they would follow our directions in carrying out the grant?"

5. Some funders, in lieu or in addition to any one-to-one responses to questions, are increasingly offering informational webinars or conference calls about the RFP. There is an expectation that every serious applicant will participate in this opportunity. In addition, there may well be information gleaned from these resources that might not be available elsewhere. Attend!

CHAPTER CHECKLIST

☐ Use the set of seven questions in the chapter to help you "decode" any RFP you are considering.

☐ Remember to look for funding priorities and funding limitations throughout the RFP, not just in the introduction section.

☐ Pay special attention to the funding criteria if the funder provides that.

☐ If permitted, contact the funder with questions you may have.

So, how did the Nale Foundation and Hengema County get their names? They are anagrams of the authors' last names.

CHAPTER 5

··
···

THREE FICTITIOUS ORGANIZATIONS
SERVING THE AGING

CHAPTER OVERVIEW

In this chapter, you will learn about three fictitious (but realistic) organizations serving the aged. Each is seeking a grant from the equally fictitious Nale Foundation.

Introduction

We created three fictitious aging service organizations so we could create equally fictitious sections of their grant applications as exemplars throughout this book. We expect these exemplars will be helpful by putting the general suggestions and tips about each section into a realistic context. We hope they will help you frame your own sections of a grant proposal. After the descriptions of these agencies, we list the chapters that have examples based on their applications.

Keep in mind that the exemplars we will be providing are not the only way the various sections of the grant could be written. You may find it better to use a different approach or tone with a real funder. You might also find that the exemplar does not match your writing style, or you may think of an even better way to respond. There is never one right way to respond to a request for proposal (RFP).

The fictitious agencies are the following:

1. **Nale City Multiservice Senior Center** ("Nale City MSC"), a governmentally sponsored, multiservice senior center seeking a grant to develop a fall-prevention program.

2. **Friends and Neighbors Home Health Care Agency** ("Friends and Neighbors"), a community-based, not-for-profit home care agency seeking a grant to improve communication between staff and family members.

3. **Many Churches Skilled Nursing and Rehabilitation Center** ("Many Churches"), a religiously based nursing home seeking a grant to create a facility that is more "person-centered," using culture-change principles.

Each of these fictitious aging service providers is completely invented by the authors and no association with an existing entity with a similar name or similar grant interest is implied.

Nale City Multiservice Senior Center (Governmental Entity)

The Nale City Multiservice Senior Center (Nale City MSC) is one of seven senior centers located throughout the county. Nale City MSC serves as the focal point for services for over 500 older adults from throughout the largest city in the county. It not only provides meals but also information and assistance, recreation, education, and limited transportation services. While some services require participants to pay a cost-share, most are free and there is no membership fee. Participants are active and generally do not have major mobility or self-care issues. The center is funded by both Nale County and Nale City.

Two years ago the center was remodeled and expanded to reflect the changing needs of aging baby boomers. Now that the physical plant is complete, the center staff is concentrating on expanding the range of services offered by the center.

A survey of the participants indicated there was a strong interest in the center offering a fall-prevention program. The center would like to pursue a grant to allow it to develop an evidenced-based program in this area.

Illustrative exemplars of the sections of the grant this agency might write when applying to the Nale Foundation are found in Chapter 7 ("How to Create an Effective Abstract and Executive Summary"), Chapter 12 ("Devising a Functional and Accurate Budget") and Chapter 13 ("Corporate Capability and Qualifications").

Friends and Neighbors Home Health Care Agency
(Not-for-Profit Home Care Entity)

The Friends and Neighbors Home Health Care Agency (Friends and Neighbors), located in Nale City, is a not-for-profit founded and incorporated in 1994 by two friends who saw a home care need in their community. Both nurses, they first did most of the work themselves. They gradually added staff and recruited volunteers. The agency now employs social workers, nurses, a case manager, a physical therapist, and an occupational therapist, as well as home health aides and companions. It also has a part-time volunteer coordinator and about 50 volunteers. Their active board of directors has grown to 15 community leaders.

Friends and Neighbors is a freestanding agency that serves both Medicare and Medicaid clients. Last year the agency served 450 older people and persons of all ages with disabilities.

Because a recent customer satisfaction survey showed some client discontent with how staff communicated with them, Friends and Neighbors is looking for grant funding to train their staff on effective communication techniques with clients and their families.

Sections of the grant this agency might write when applying to the Nale Foundation are found in Chapter 8 ("Developing an Effective Needs Assessment"), Chapter 10 ("Evaluation and Logic Models") and Chapter 11 ("Building a Logical Work Plan (Methodology) and Timeline").

Many Churches Skilled Nursing and Rehabilitation Center (Not-for-Profit)

The Many Churches Skilled Nursing and Rehabilitation Center (Many Churches) is a traditionally designed 200-bed not-for-profit nursing home and rehabilitation center that has been in operation since the 1960s when it was first formed by a coalition of churches. It is located in a rural area of Hengema County. It has maintained a positive reputation in the community with excellent surveys and a 4-star federal rating.

With a new executive director and a newly re-energized board, Many Churches is seeking to modernize the way it delivers care. First, it is interested in replicating some of the concepts inherent in the culture-change movement, including the work of the Green House model and the Pioneer Network. These groups call for moving away from institutional provider-driven models to more consumer-driven models that embrace flexibility and self-determination (Grabowski et al., 2014; Pioneer Network, 2015; Shara, Siders, & Dannifer, 2011).

Many Churches, therefore, is seeking a grant to support the costs of minor modifications in its plant to make it more person-centered by adding kitchens and dining areas to three nursing units. The grant application will seek partial funding to convert underutilized space on each of the units, so that the eating experience can be more homelike, giving residents on those units the option to have meals in their unit and not have to travel to the large main dining room unless they choose to do so. One board member, a builder, will donate the cost of labor for the minor renovations needed for these changes. Another has pledged to donate stoves and exhaust fans. Separate fundraising will cover the cost of materials. Grant funds are therefore needed only to provide small refrigerators, cooking equipment, tables, and staff training.

Many Churches has an ongoing, but separate, capital campaign for physical renovations that will be referenced in the proposal as matching funds for the project.

Sections of the grant this agency might write when applying to the Nale Foundation are found in Chapter 9 ("How to Create Goals and Objectives") and Chapter 14 ("Letters of Intent").

PART III

WRITING THE
PROPOSAL

CHAPTER 6

UNDERSTANDING PROPOSAL COMPONENTS
AND THEIR LINKAGES

CHAPTER OVERVIEW

In this chapter, you will find:

- A summary chart depicting the most common components of a proposal and their purposes

- Succinct definitions of the parts of most grant proposals

- Critical information on how the different components link together

- The dangers of writing sections independently

Introduction

We are finally in the part of the book in which you learn the techniques for writing your proposal. The following table provides a graphic view of common proposal components:

Common Grant Components and Purposes

NAME OF COMPONENT	CONTENT
Abstract /Executive Summary	A short description of the entire proposal
Needs Assessment or Rationale	Why is there is a need for the grant?
Goals and Objectives	What will be done?
Work Plan or Methodology	How will the project be done?
Timeline	When will parts of the project be done?
Evaluation	How can the effectiveness of the project be assessed?
Budget	What are the costs of the project?
Common additions—letters of support, not-for-profit status, financial reports, resumes	Why is your organization ideally qualified to carry out the work of the grant?

This table is accurate for most proposals. However, each request for proposal (RFP) may have its own distinctive features, requirements, and names for each category. Therefore, when writing a specific proposal, follow the grant guidelines as to what should go in each section rather than what is shown here. **The RFP is always right!**

We have provided a separate chapter on the parts of the grant instead of simply defining them when we detail how to write them. We chose this approach to emphasize that they are not separate components that can be written in isolation, independent of each other. They must integrate. Therefore, the section called "How the Grant Components Link Together" is the most important one in this chapter.

Abstract and/or Executive Summary

The **abstract** is the short, objective summation of your grant. It is usually very short: less than one page, or even one short paragraph. It is the final version of the planning abstract discussed in earlier chapters,

The **executive summary** is a longer, more detailed version of the abstract, often running one to five pages, depending on the length of the proposal. Some funders require both, some only one. When the RFP requires only one of these introductory sections, the terms are used interchangeably. The purpose is the same: to provide an overview of what the reviewer will find in the full proposal.

We consider these two sections as critical components of the grant proposal. You only have one chance at a first impression. If either section is carelessly written, unclear, or simply not compelling, the reviewer may have an initial negative reaction that might be hard to overcome.

Needs Assessment or Rationale

The needs assessment is where you provide the carefully researched and factual description of the problem that the grant funds will resolve. Occasionally, the term "rationale" is used instead of the term "needs assessment." More commonly, the rationale is where you describe why you picked a specific solution to the problem. The two are often covered in the same section, often called "Evidence-Based Documentation" (based on solid, previous research or data), which is almost always needed to make a compelling needs assessment and rationale. Chapter 8, "Developing an Effective Needs Assessment," provides a detailed discussion of the concept of *evidence-based.*

If this section is weak, no matter how strong other sections are, you have not justified the need to spend money on your proposed project, and the funder will opt to spend its limited funds elsewhere.

Goals and Objectives

Both goals and objectives are intended to describe the purpose of a proposed project succinctly and clearly. When developed well, goals and objectives will allow the funder to understand the specific purpose and scope of your project and what the grant can specifically be expected to accomplish.

Goals are commonly defined as global statements of what you intend to achieve if the project is funded.

Objectives are commonly defined as measurable statements of what outcomes you expect to achieve by meeting your goals.

Each is usually written very concisely, often as a phrase starting with the word "To." An example of an overall goal might be:

> To enrich the quality of life for rural elders by establishing discussion groups and learning opportunities in 10 rural libraries in XX County.

An example of one objective related to this goal might be:

> To provide 12 hours of distance-learning training on adult learning pedagogy to three to six staff and volunteers from each library using evidence-based training materials and professional trainers, as detailed in subsequent sections.

Note the great degree of specificity in the objective. This specificity is important not only because the reviewers expect it, but also because it creates a solid base for planning your work on the grant and for the evaluation.

Work Plan or Methodology

Together, these items are where you show your plan of action to achieve the goals of the grant. The **work plan** (the term used more often with operational grants) and the **methodology** (the term used more often with research-oriented grants) are the sections in which you tell the reviewer how, when, and with whom you will complete the proposal. Most RFPs specify what kind of information and how much detail are required in this section. In a typical grant for program operations, some of the major elements to be included might include overall operation of the project (staff training, purchase of supplies, contracts with collaborators and partners, etc.), participant recruitment, things to be done as part of the project, on-going process evaluation, data collection, and the evaluation itself.

Timeline

The **timeline** is a table showing what major activities will be done to meet the goals and objectives, when they will take place, and who will be doing them.

Evaluation

The evaluation section of a proposal varies more from proposal to proposal than any other section of the grant. It may be very short and simple in a small foundation grant and easily accomplishable with your existing staff, or it can be astoundingly complex in a federal research grant and require significant support from expert academic researchers. For projects written by aging service organizations, most evaluation requirements fall somewhere between these two extremes.

No matter the size or complexity, the evaluation section is where you detail for the reviewer how you plan to show whether the grant activities met their goals or not. This kind of evaluation is known as an outcome evaluation.

Many RFPs require you to conduct a process evaluation as well. A process evaluation assesses how well you are completing each task and is a way for the reviewer to see how you will be able to determine, while the grant is still active, whether you are on track to meet your goals.

Budget

A budget is not a simple division of the amount of money available. It is financial Russian roulette to think like this: "Hmmm, the grant will award up to $50,000, so let's do it this way: $30,000 for salaries, fringe, and overhead, and $20,000 for project expenses," without calculating your actual costs.

In our opinion, the budget is not a separate section to write only after the narrative is done, although many grant books suggest you do it that way. While, of course, the budget is *completed* only after the entire proposal is written, the budget is a key component of your proposal planning, and you need to work from the very start to project the expenses you will incur. After all, it is the rough budget calculations that will let you know if you should move forward with the proposal!

As we discuss in Chapter 12 (Devising a Functional and Accurate Budget), a good budget will develop directly from your work plan. As your deliverables and outcomes are finalized, the budget will also change. Budgeting will require that you work closely with your fiscal staff as you formulate your proposal.

Common Additions: Boilerplate Items, Corporate Capability, Letters of Support, and Resumes

Leaving the gathering of these materials—which are required in most grant applications—for the last minute is likely to create weaker content in these sections. When you are consumed with the challenges of writing a proposal, it is very easy to forget that weaknesses in any of these areas can downgrade a proposal as much as any weakness in the narrative or budget. Consider their preparation as important as anything else you do in the grant preparation process.

Boilerplate: In grant writing, *boilerplate* is the term generally used for a required list of forms. Most commonly these forms include documentation of 501(c)(3) status, the latest audited financial report, and a list of board members and their affiliations. A grant "face page" or first page form requiring detailed information is often required as well and is part of the boilerplate.

Corporate Capability: Many RFPs require a specific section called corporate capability. This section may have other names, but it is the section in which the organization describes itself. It is also a major marketing opportunity, as this is where an organization makes the case for itself as the ideal entity to conduct the grant. Components of this section are typically a mission statement, catchment area, and proof of past experience in the proposed area, or other reasons why the organization is qualified for and worthy of funding. We discuss the concept of corporate capability in detail in Chapter 13.

Letters of Support: Some RFPs require these letters from collaborators to assure the funder that the collaboration is real. Additional letters are sometimes required or optional and provide an opportunity to show what other organizations, prominent individuals, or elected officials think of the proposal.

Resumes: Resumes for key staff are requirements in almost all grant proposals and are usually in an attachment or the last pages of a proposal. It is effective to tailor them to the grant. Some suggestions:

1. Edit resumes so they focus on skills and/or experience relevant to the proposed project. If sent in print, relevant skills can be highlighted. Another way to highlight relevant information is to add a sentence or two at the top of the resume. For example, for the resume of a project director in a proposal focused on starting a child care program in a continuing care retirement community (CCRC), the top summary sentence might say:

> Director of Programs at XYZ Continuing Care Retirement Community for 8 years, with an MS in gerontology, a BA in early childhood education, and 2 years of previous experience in running intergenerational programs at a senior center involving preschool visitations.

Details on these experiences would be provided in the body of the resume.

2. When including the resume of someone with a long academic background, tailor the information by highlighting previous research in the area to be evaluated, if possible. If nothing is highly relevant, stress relevant research experience.

Also, if space is an issue, consider shortening academic resumes to two or three pages, by listing one article in each specific area and noting that there are six more available upon request. Presentations at conferences should also be included.

Logic Models

Logic models began to appear in the social science literature during the 1970s and quickly began appearing in the scientific and applied disciplines. It was, however, the 1990s when they began to appear as a requirement of RFPs. While they are now generally a regular requirement of many larger grant funders, many smaller and local foundations still do not require grant writers to develop a logic model as part of their proposal. However, the trend toward logic models is likely to reach smaller foundations as well.

A logic model visually depicts and describes what your proposal is all about and what it will accomplish. There are literally hundreds of logic model templates but all contain the following three basic components:

> **Inputs → Outputs → Outcomes/Impacts**

Inputs are the resources and investments that go into the proposal. The **outputs** are the activities, services, and/or products that will reach the individuals, organizations, or communities that are the focus of your proposal. The **outcomes/impacts** are the results or changes that will occur as a result of the activities supported by your proposal.

Understanding How the Sections Relate to Each Other and the Importance of Integrating Them

Each proposal component builds upon the other. There should be a logical flow in which information from each section is used in the next section, as shown in this simple flow chart:

> **Needs Assessment/Rationale → Goals →**
> **Methodology → Evaluation → Budget**

When you have a good needs assessment or rationale, you have described a critical problem that needs to be solved. The goals section will explain to what extent you intend to address the problem in a measurable manner. The methodology or work plan section will then discuss how, in practical terms, you are going to tackle the problem. For example, you may increase staffing and/or carry out new activities. The evaluation will assess how well your methods have met the goals and therefore ameliorated the problem stated in the need. The budget is a statement of the costs to accomplish all of these activities. The logic model will show this flow in a graphic form.

When these sections are written in a uncoordinated manner, this logical flow of content is interrupted and make the project seem unclear at best or inconsistent at worst. In an ideal world, one person would work on the entire proposal. However, time constraints often make this impossible. Therefore, if there is a team approach to writing the grant, there needs to be frequent communication among all the team members so the wording and concepts can flow logically from section to section.

CHAPTER 7

....

HOW TO CREATE AN EFFECTIVE ABSTRACT
AND EXECUTIVE SUMMARY

CHAPTER OVERVIEW

In this chapter, you will learn about:

- The similarities and the differences between the abstract and the executive summary

- The strategic importance of these opening sections

- Writing tips

- An illustrative sample of an abstract and an executive summary from the Nale City Senior Center

Introduction

The abstract and/or the executive summary is your one and only chance at a first impression. If either section is carelessly written, unclear, or simply not compelling, the reviewer will have an initial negative reaction that will be hard to overcome. Therefore, no section of the proposal should be more carefully written and reviewed than these sections.

An **abstract** is a very short, objective summation of your grant. It should fit on one page and may even be just one short paragraph.

We have seen some instances in which a very brief abstract is in a fill-in-the-blank format. An example of that is:

_____ (Name of applicant) requests funds to_____

_____

_____.

Expected outcomes are

(1)_____ (2) _____ (3) _____

Outcomes will be measured by _____

_____

_____ . The total financial support requested

is $ _____. There is $ _____ pledged from

other resources.

If you are stuck on how to organize an abstract, this template may prove useful. If you use it as a model, adapt it to meet your needs.

An **executive summary** is a longer, more detailed version of the abstract, often running one to five pages, depending on the length of the proposal. Some funders require both types of summaries, some only one.

When the request for proposal (RFP) requires only one of these introductory sections, the terms are used interchangeably. The purpose is the same: to provide an overview of what the reviewer will find in the full proposal.

Note: To avoid extra verbiage, we use the term **executive summary** in the rest of this chapter to refer to both the abstract and the executive summary.

The Marketing Importance of the Executive Summary

As noted at the beginning of this chapter, the executive summary is your one and only chance at a first impression. Therefore, no section of the proposal should be more carefully written, reviewed, and polished. In addition, larger foundations and governmental funders often assign reviewers to proposals based on the executive summary. Lack of clarity in the executive summary will hinder the reviewer who is tasked with evaluating your proposal.

Three Tips for Writing Executive Summaries

1. Use the wording in the RFP so the reviewer can readily see that the overall priorities and interests of the funder are part of your proposal.

For example, one of the authors wrote a successful grant to the Federal Corporation on National and Community Service (CNCS) in response to an RFP stating that the CNCS wanted to *harness the skills and experience of baby boomers and other older adults in community service.* The executive summary for this funded proposal opened with:

"___ (name of agency) will harness the experience of __ (#) of baby boomers in service by_____."

Such judicious (not continual, which can be annoying) echoing of words or themes from the RFP helps the reviewers see that you are on track with the expectations of the funder.

2. Write your abstract and executive summary early in the grant-writing process. Some grant-writing trainers advise clients to write these sections last as a way of ensuring consistency. We disagree. A preliminary draft abstract is, in our opinion, the most effective tool for getting early feedback from colleagues (see Chapter 2) and therefore needs to be written, in draft form, at the beginning. However, remember that a draft abstract *must* change to a final executive summary as you write the rest of the narrative.

3. Envision the abstract and executive summary as a *constantly evolving* work in progress, with updates continually made to reflect changes in the grant narrative. We suggest reading and revising it each time you start and finish writing text for the following three reasons:

a.   This process will prevent you from going off on tangents from your core concepts or, conversely, will alert you that you need to add an additional core concept to your abstract or executive summary. For example, you may add an major new objective as you refine the proposal, and you will now need to add it to the executive summary.

b.   You will be making changes in the executive summary as they are needed; for example, you wouldn't say that you will serve 300 elders in the abstract if the narrative and budget say that you will serve 250 elders.

c.   You will be more likely to include a particularly compelling phrase or sentence in the executive summary about the need or value of the project. Sometimes as you are writing, you come up with an ideal phrase or sentence. By constantly revising your executive summary, you will be reminded to add this phrase to it. For example, if you are working on a grant for an intergenerational oral history project in which students interview elders about their life stories, you might decide to use the phrase "our seniors are our living legacy" in your narrative. If you have a theme phrase such as this one, you will want to include it in your executive summary.

Illustrative Executive Summary

As you will remember from Chapter 5 ("Three Fictitious Organizations Serving the Aging"), the Nale City Multiservice Senior Center (Nale City MSC) is seeking a grant to develop a fall-prevention program.

The specific requirements of the Nale Foundation for writing the executive summary are the following: *Provide an overview of your project. Include the project name, why the project is needed, the goal of the project and how you will accomplish the project goals. Provide your start and end date as well as the dollar amount of your grant request.*

Consonant with the goals of the Nale Foundation to improve care of older people, the Nale City Multiservice Senior Center (Nale City MSC) requests $20,843 to develop a fall-prevention program called Stop Falls Now (SFN). We will serve 60 seniors in six waves of training in Nale City. SFN will run for 2 years, starting September __ .

The project is needed because 10% of emergency medical technician (EMT) responses to calls for older adults in our area were related to falls, creating excess disability and avoidable health care costs. This 10% is higher than the state average.

Numerous studies of SFN have appeared in leading academic journals that supply empirical evidence of program efficacy (see Needs Assessment for details). Therefore, our primary outcome is to reduce falls in our participants by the same 20% rate seen in SFN.

In Months 1–5, we will train staff, recruit 10 elders into a pilot study, and evaluate the program via pre- and posttests and a process evaluation. In Months 6–15, we will recruit and train the additional 50 elders in five training waves, each time evaluating impact by using quasi-experimental design and recruiting the next wave. In Months 16–18, we will complete the evaluation and run our "Fall-Prevention Fiesta" fundraiser to help support the project after grant funding ends.

Because of the necessity for this project, Nale City MSC pledges to sustain the project by continuing to serve about 60 additional elders each year. We will use sliding-scale program fees, board-designated funds, and money from our annual "Fall-Prevention Fiesta" to support the program.

Note: Be sure that you are including everything in the executive summary that is required. The Nale Foundation did not, for example, require that objectives be included, but other foundations do.

CHAPTER CHECKLIST

☐ Are you updating your abstract and executive summary as you write to reflect changes and to ensure that they reflect the actual content in the proposal?

☐ Do you use wording in the RFP to explain your project?

☐ When appropriate, did you use a compelling and/or unique phrase to set your proposal apart in the abstract?

☐ Did you follow the required template or include information on goals, objectives, and concepts?

CHAPTER 8

....

DEVELOPING AN EFFECTIVE
NEEDS ASSESSMENT

CHAPTER OVERVIEW

In this chapter, you will learn:

- The definition of a needs assessment

- The importance of the term "evidence-based" and how to use an evidence base in your needs assessment

- How to research your topic so you have compelling data to share

- Tips for writing the needs assessment

- An ethical dilemma concerning the needs assessment

- Exemplar of the needs assessment of a fictitious proposal

Introduction

Definition of Needs Assessment or Rationale

The **needs assessment** is the carefully researched and factual description of the problem that grant funds will resolve. Often it includes a **rationale** (a description of why the approach you plan to use is a good one to alleviate the problem). Sometimes the rationale is requested in another section of the request for proposal (RFP).

The needs assessment answers the question, "Why is this grant needed and important?" Sometimes it may seem as if the need is self-evident or already clearly stated in the RFP, but that is never an excuse for not providing a clear statement of why your grant is important. Yes, funders may understand the problem and may even have included a description of the need for it in the RFP, but they want to assess *your* knowledge of the need and the nature and complexity of the need in your area. Show them your mastery of this area.

RFPs, as we have said before, differ widely. Among the many names for this section are needs, background, rationale, and significance. There may be others.

For most grants, including those focused on aging, your needs assessment might cover four areas:

1. The needs of a particular group (in our case, elders).

2. The needs of society (town, county, state, country) as a whole.

3. The need to reduce societal or governmental costs.

4. Documentation that the need is not already being well met. If you have done an external review of your concept, as suggested in Chapter 2, you should already be aware of any existing similar programs addressing the need.

Understanding the Importance of the Term "Evidence-Based"

"Evidence-based" means that there is empirical research supporting the need for a program as well as the efficacy of the program you are going to use to address the need. You need to demonstrate a need for a project, and you may also need (depending on the funder) evidence that the intervention you propose has worked before.

While not every funder requires evidence-based data, it is best to provide such information anyway. Evidence-based information is required for most grant applications at the federal level, and we expect that it will be required in all grants in the near future, as will be discussed later in this section.

Consider the difference between these two statements:

> It is well-known that isolated elders are at risk for health problems.

> *versus*

> Social isolation among older people has an adverse impact on health and well-being (see Findley, 2003).

The first statement is unacceptable in a well-written needs assessment. Such a statement is merely an unsupported statement of opinion. By contrast, the second statement is appropriate because it is backed up with a professional citation or data from a reputable source. Another way to use data in a needs assessment is to draw on statistical sources such as the U.S. Census Bureau or a state department of health or aging.

You can strengthen your needs assessment by using *comparative data* showing why the project is needed in your specific location. Remember, as an effective grant writer, you are always answering the question, "Why should the funder choose your proposal over others?" In an example that might be used in an application to the Nale Foundation (see Chapter 4) to obtain funds to develop an adult care programs, the needs assessment might include strong comparative statements like these:

- According to the 2010 Census, Hengema County has the third highest percentage of people aged 80 years old and older of the 40 counties in our state.

- Neighboring August County, with a similar total population, has six adult day programs, while Hengema County has only two, each of which is more than 30 miles away from the one proposed. (Source: *August County Human Services Report*, 2016; *Hengema County Services Report*, 2016).

Remember, it is also important to explain why the intervention (what you will do to address the problem) is appropriate. Therefore, include data that show the proposed intervention is effective, that is, has an evidence base and is cost effective.

An example of a paragraph using evidence-based data in this way is:

> We propose to retrofit 20 traditional nursing home rooms into "culture-changed" (sometimes referred to as "person-centered care") homes because recent research of similar conversions has shown that this model improved psycho-social care compared to traditional nursing homes (e.g., see Brownie & Nancarrow, 2013). Specifically, Brownie and Nancarrow (2013) reported positive outcomes, with few negative consequences, across a range of interventions that were all shown to improve the quality of life of residents and reduce staff turnover.

This would be an adequate evidence base for a small- to medium-sized proposal. If your entire proposal is only a few pages, you might include just the first one. If it is a large, complex proposal, you would need to supply even more documentation from more than one source.

When possible, you would also use a cost-effectiveness analysis, defined as "a method for assessing the gains in health relative to the costs of different health interventions" (Jamison et al., 2006, p. 40). Here is an example of a cost-effectiveness analysis from a proposal to add technology to the services of a home care agency:

> We chose our "Tech at Home" design to keep people safe at home because other programs using it have shown that it has a far lower cost than other programs also designed to ensure that frail elders living alone are safe. Based on the data from other "Tech at Home" programs and cost reports on home care services, we project that our total unit cost is $40–50 per visit using "Tech at Home" as opposed to $176 for the standard in-home visit (see Dvorak, S., 2014). Study:

Telehealth Can Save $100 or More Per Visit. *FierceHealthIT*, http://www.fiercehealthit.com/story/study-telehealth-can-save-100-or-more-visit/2014-12-15).

Note: If you are writing a very small grant to a community agency and have very limited space for a needs assessment, you will need to consolidate and simplify your information on the evidence for your project.

For large grants, you might also need to show that your project design is based on previous research; that is, you cannot usually just say, "I would like to try this and see if it helps the problem." In fact, if you are applying to the Administration on Community Living (ACL), which now includes the Administration on Aging (AoA), you have to satisfy specific, stringent criteria on what constitutes an evidence-based program:

In October 2016, the ACL refined the older AoA definitions of evidence-based programs. For all funding applications, ACL now requires adherence to the following guidelines (Boutaugh et al., 2015, p. 108):

AoA/ACL Evidence-Based Criteria

• Demonstrated through evaluation to be effective for improving the health and well-being or reducing disease, disability, or injury among older adults.

• Proven effective with older adult population, using experimental or quasi-experimental design.

• Research results published in a peer-review journal.

• Fully translated* in one or more community site(s).

• Includes developed dissemination products that are available to the public.

*Translation in this context means "put into place." Please note that for other applications to other funding sources, this comprehensive list of criteria might not be required. However, it would be wise to use this list as a general guide.

Researching the Need

The places to look for data are as varied as grant applications. Here is a useful list of six ways to look for data to support the need for your project:

1. The Internet. Be careful to cite from only reputable and relevant sites or blogs rather than just any sites that come up in search results, many of which may be unreliable. The value of the Internet is not in any piece of information it has, but rather the way it can lead you to sites that are reputable, such as reports from governmental bodies, well-known research entities, and peer-reviewed journals. Stick to sources that the reviewer can respect.

   Many libraries have search engines available (e.g., JSTOR), which will allow you to search the full range of academic journals that publish research articles on behavioral health, and social topics. If working at a small office or at home, use your browser to find appropriate journals, such as *The Gerontologist* and other highly respected journals in the field. Once on the site, you may find that a search engine leads you to the reference you need.

2. Use your own data, waiting lists, shortages, and so forth. For example, in an application for funds to add an additional day services program, you might use a sentence such as, "Our current adult day services program has 20 people on its waiting list for the last 3 years, enough to fill the new proposed adult day care center." Your own satisfaction surveys might also be used (as in the exemplar at the end of this chapter).

3. If you are planning an educational program, consider providing the existing level of knowledge and compare it to what level you need to ensure an improved status. (You may need to do your own pretest, ideally using an accepted measure to do get the data you need.)

4. Include federal, state, and local data in your area of interest, such as U.S. Census reports, Area Agency on Aging (AAA) plans, and various state reports.

5. An ideal way for a small local agency to find reputable articles is to request help from university faculty. Departments of sociology, nursing, psychology, medicine, and physical therapy usually have faculty with a specialty in aging and may steer you to the most salient articles. If you are very lucky, they may identify a student willing to do this research as part of a term paper.

6. State and national trade associations often produce reports that may also be appropriate.

Six Tips on Writing Effective Needs Assessment

1. Remember that you must describe the needs of the people you serve—not the needs of your own agency. This issue is discussed in more detail in Chapter 9 ("How to Create Goals and Objectives"), but the main concept can be seen in the difference between these two sentences:

> Our agency does not have the funds to cover the salary of our activities coordinator.

> *versus*

> Based on research showing that meaningful activities enhance mental health [citation here], we need to increase our activity programs so that all participants in our senior center have a choice of two different activities during their time with us.

Clearly, the first sentence is not as compelling as the second: Addressing salary needs is not as compelling as meeting elder needs. Further, if you have the grant, you will have additional dollars for the salary of an activities coordinator, and you may be able to plan a way to sustain the income after funding ends.

2. Funders will not be interested in solving the problems in one small nonprofit, so it is ideal if you can explain in your needs assessment how your project will ultimately benefit the larger

community. Dissemination to other sites is a typical way to achieve this community-wide benefit. In this case, letters of support from other sites will be, of course, helpful, as would a statement from a regional association confirming that it will help to replicate your project.

3. As noted above, use comparative statistics when they work in your favor. Consider the difference in the power of these two sentences:

In Nale City, 35% of people over age 65 live in poverty.

versus

In Nale City, 35% of people over age 65 live in poverty, although the countywide poverty level for people over age 65 is only 20%.

4. Be leery of using national or statewide data for a very local project, as reviewers may think (accurately or not) that these data may not be applicable to your area. Most Area Agencies on Aging will have local data that will support the need for your project.

5. Worth repeating: **Use only reputable sources and citations.**

6. If you cannot find data that support the need for your project, change the focus of your application. Proposals that do not address a documented need should not be funded!

Note: Tip #6 does not necessarily mean that you need to rework your whole proposal. Suppose, for example, you want funds for diabetes prevention and management for seniors, but the incidence rate for diabetes in your large county is far less than the state average. You don't necessarily need to jettison your project. Look further before giving up by doing the following:

a.   Explore data sources in more depth. For example, look for diabetes rates for people over 65 instead of the entire population.

b.   Reframe your project to address an alternative, but related, documented need such as obesity rates.

c.   Look for very regional data to see if you can show that there are specific pockets within your area, such as one city in which diabetes rates are higher than the rest of the county, and focus your project there.

As with all sections of a proposal, make it easier for the reviewer by organizing the text so it reflects, in the same order requested, all of the components requested and it covers all of the items used to evaluate the proposal.

Ethical Dilemma 2: What if your needs assessment reveals that other entities are running similar programs successfully or those similar programs were tried and failed locally? You can hide these facts from the potential funder. Should you?

It is always tempting not to mention potentially negative information, but in a situation like this, you should not give in to that temptation. First, you have an ethical responsibility not to waste precious grant monies on a duplicative program or one that is likely to fail. Second, it is possible that a reviewer will know about other programs or articles about them and their relative success or failure. If you omit the fact that there are other successful programs, you run the risk of being perceived as untrustworthy. That perception can keep you from being funded.

However, if a program has been tried and not proven successful, you might—*under limited, ideal circumstances*—have an opportunity to use that failure to your advantage. For example, you may be able to highlight what you have learned from an analysis of a failed program and explain how your own project is different. If you can address the issue of a previous failure convincingly and with accuracy, you may be able to write something like this:

An agency in neighboring XYZ City tried a similar program 3 years ago and was not successful. In preparation for this proposal, we met with the management staff of that agency to learn what went wrong. They reported that their per-person cost was too high, which drove potential participants away, and their recruitment efforts were inadequate. Therefore, despite high satisfaction rates among participants and promising results, they closed the program.

We have benefited from these insights and propose to (a) lower the per-person cost by 50% because we will have matching corporate funds and (b) plan a far more robust recruitment plan, as noted in the Methodology section. Because we have addressed specific weaknesses in an otherwise well-received project, we expect this project will be highly successful.

Illustrative Needs Assessment

As you will remember from Chapter 5 ("Three Fictitious Organizations Serving the Aging"), The Friends and Neighbors Home Health Care Agency (Friends and Neighbors) is seeking a grant from the Nale Foundation to develop a training program to train its staff on effective communication techniques with challenging clients (especially those with dementia) and their families.

The requirements of this section in the Nale Foundation RFP are:

> *Tell us why this project is needed in Nale County. Provide data that document the need. How are you going to address this need? Are there organizations or programs in your community that are successfully addressing the same need? If there are, how will you work together?*

Sample Statement of Need

The need for this caring communication training program is documented by a customer satisfaction survey, community and client input, and solid research data:

1. Survey: Each year the Friends and Neighbors Home Health Care Agency (Friends and Neighbors) conducts customer satisfaction surveys of its 500 clients and 300 family members. For the past 3 years, surveys have shown a decline in satisfaction in the way aides communicate with clients and their families. Specifically, we had an 85% satisfaction in this area 3 years ago, and we are now down to 65%. Staff satisfaction rates have also decreased from 70% to 50%.

2. Community Input: Informal discussions with the staff of the other home care agency, the three nursing homes, and the one assisted living facility in the county revealed similar downward trends in client and staff satisfaction. Therefore, other agencies are eager to help us design this training and replicate it in their own agencies once we have developed it at Friends and Neighbors. (Six letters of support documenting this shared problem as well as a willingness to work with us to develop the project are being sent in a separate mailed attachment.)

3. Impact of Family Dissatisfaction: We know that this kind of dissatisfaction has an effect on caregivers: Poor relationships with the staff have been found to be predictive of family members' depression (Brody, Dempsey, & Pruchno, 1990; Cassie & Cassie, 2012), anxiety (Pruchno & Kleban, 1993), and emotional stress related to caregiving (Pearlin, Mullan, Semple, & Skaff, 1990; Yaffee et al., 2002). Since the rate of family caregiver depression and anxiety is already known to be high in people who provide care for family members (Kim, Chang, Rose, & Kim, 2011), addressing this problem is important not only for the clients receiving care but for caregivers as well. Given the high rate of family caregivers in our county (25% according to the Nale County Area Agency on Aging) compared to 21% of households in the United States (Centers for Disease Control and Prevention, 2011), the need for this project is particularly appropriate for elders in our area.

4. Impact on Staff: We also know that troubled relationships with families are a likely source of distress for staff as well (Pillemer & Hudson, 1993). These results are consistent with the general finding that few aspects of life are more distressing than interpersonal conflict (Sternberg & Dobson, 1987).

How Will We Address the Need?

We will modify an existing evidence-based training program called Partners in Caregiving (PIC; Cox, 2002). This training program has a strong professional evaluation: A randomized, controlled evaluation of the PIC program demonstrated improved attitudes for both groups, a reduced intention to quit for staff, and less family conflict with staff, specifically for families of residents with dementia in nursing homes (Pillemer & Suitor, 2002). Another study (Robison & Pillemer, 2007) found similar positive results in special care units in nursing homes.

We will work with a consultant who is familiar with both this program and home care to modify the program so that it is applicable to the home care setting in our region. We will then develop and implement it in our home care setting for 200 staff members and 100 family members, evaluate it, make refinements as needed, and then offer it for use in to all aging service providers in the county.

Are there organizations or programs in your community that are successfully addressing the same need? If there are, how will you work together?

As noted above, this project addresses a common problem of reduced staff and family satisfaction in Nale County, but no one has yet attempted to address it. With this project, we will test and refine it first at Friends and Neighbors and then conduct training for other aging service providers in the county. As can be seen from appended letters of agreement from five aging service providers and detailed in our Methodology section, each provider will donate the time of staff to serve on the advisory committee for this project and has committed to using the training in Year 2.

CHAPTER CHECKLIST

☐ Does your needs assessment explain the need using evidence-based data and comparative data when applicable?

☐ Are your citations from highly reputable sources?

☐ If applicable, did you include some benefit to the community at large as well as to your own agency?

☐ Did you describe why the intervention you are proposing is appropriate, using an evidence base?

☐ Did you cover all of the items and questions mentioned in the RFP?

CHAPTER 9

....

HOW TO CREATE GOALS AND OBJECTIVES

CHAPTER OVERVIEW

In this chapter, you will learn:

- The definition of goals and objectives

- Tips for writing effective goals and objectives

- An ethical dilemma concerning goals and objectives

- The needs assessment

- Exemplars of goals and objectives

Introduction

Goals and objectives are the heart of your proposal. Everything you want to accomplish relates closely to how your goals and objectives are written. Get them right!

Definitions

A **goal** is usually defined as a rather global statement of what you intend to achieve if the project is successfully completed.

Objectives are usually highly measurable and specific statements of how you intend to achieve the overall goal.

The goal and objectives share the same general purposes in a grant proposal:

1. To allow the funder to understand the intent and scope of your project.

2. To help you develop a framework for your methodology.

3. To develop the criteria by which your project can be evaluated.

Therefore, the goal and objectives should clearly relate to the needs assessment, the methodology, and the evaluation. We are repeating the interrelationship of these grant components because they are so critical to the success of a proposal.

The goal and objectives are usually written in the infinitive form, with the word "To" starting the sentence. Here is an example that comes from the kind of proposal a state association might write to serve its entire membership. In this case, the membership consists of nursing home providers. (This example is derived from a successful statewide grant application written by one of the authors.)

Goal

To enhance the quality of life for approximately 1,000 nursing home residents with dementia in 15 nursing homes in XX state, by reducing physical and psychological stress during bathing.

Objectives

1. To train 100 nursing home aides from at least 15 nursing homes in XX state so that they can implement the evidence-based and award-winning "Bathing Without a Battle" training intervention (Gozalo, Parkash, Qato, Sloane, & Mor, 2014; Radar et al., 2006) using both classroom and online training.

2. To change the bathing process for about 1,000 nursing home residents by using the Bathing Without a Battle intervention, starting in Month 6 and continuing past the life of the grant.

3. To evaluate the impact of the Bathing Without a Battle intervention on a random sample of 100 residents and staff using validated assessment measures and comparison groups at 3- and 6-month periods.

4. To report on findings at a statewide association for about 30 leadership staff of other nursing homes to encourage replication in additional sites within the state.

Four Tips for Writing Goals and Objectives

1. Use some elements of an approach such as SMART to setting goals and objectives (Doran, 1981). The SMART approach has been used in strategic planning and other business functions, and it is also helpful when structuring objectives. Other approaches might work for you as well; we provide this one as a possible template to help you form clear and complete objectives. SMART stands for:

> **Specific**—targets a specific area for improvement.
>
> **Measurable**—quantifies or at least suggests an indicator of progress.
>
> **Attainable**—ensures that an end can be achieved.
>
> **Realistic**—states what results can realistically be achieved, given available resources.
>
> **Time-related**—specifies when the result(s) can be achieved. (Not always needed when a timeline is included in the proposal. For this reason, it is not included in the objective statements used here.)

It may not be necessary or even appropriate to use each element. Use your judgment as to which ones work well for your own grant application.

2. Use wording in the request for proposal (RFP) related to expectations about funded projects in your goals and objectives when it makes sense to do so. This strategy will help the reviewer see that your proposal is appropriate for the funder. This concept was discussed in Chapter 7 ("How to Create an Effective Abstract and Executive Summary") and is equally useful when writing objectives.

3. As noted in the previous chapter, you should formulate goals and objectives in terms of client or societal outcomes, not the needs of your agency. While one hopes that grant activities will be supportive (or at least budget neutral) to the bottom line of the agency, funders want to support people, not an agency! As an example, compare the way two goals for the same project is written:

> **Weak Goal:** To increase revenue for our senior center by adding a series of weekly adult learning programs for 300 seniors in Nale City.

> Explanation: Most grantors do not want to fund your senior center—they want to provide services for your clients and other older adults.

> **Stronger Goal:** To enrich the quality of life and add socialization opportunities for about 300 seniors in Nale City by offering a challenging series of 24 weekly adult learning programs, followed by discussion groups and lunch.

4. Occasionally some RFPs will not contain a goal or objectives section. RFPs of this kind usually are requesting a specific project and expect all applicants to respond to the expectations set up in the RFP. We suggest writing your goal and objectives anyway for yourself and, if space allows, including them in your proposal. Why write them down? They help to ensure alignment among the other parts of the proposal.

Ethical Dilemma 3: If you promise a lot with your goals and objectives and show that you can do it for very little money, the funder will be impressed. So, should you overreach on your goals and objectives and underestimate your costs to help you win your grant?

Certainly, you should try to make your proposal appealing and cost effective. These are important attributes. However, setting realistic results will impress your funder more than exaggerated ones. What, for example, is wrong with stating that 100% of seniors in your weight-loss program will lose 10 pounds or more in 3 months? Why not get the edge on the competition and have the lowest budget among the applicants?

Answer: First, reviewers look carefully for overblown goals and objectives and will downgrade them. What reviewer would not look at a 100% success rate in weight loss and wonder about how much the applicant understands about the challenges of weight loss? What reviewer would see a grant that is under-resourced without thinking that the agency is not well versed in financial management? Even worse, what happens if (unlikely as it may be) you get the grant and then find that you do not have the resources to complete it?

Second, exceeding reasonable expectations will lead to problems later on if you are funded. Remember that your goals and objectives form the basis for your evaluation. If you have created unobtainable objectives, you will not be able to meet your goals. You would be setting yourself up for failure, given that almost no projects have a 100% success rate.

Illustrative Goal and Objectives

The specific requirements of the Nale Foundation for writing the goals and objectives section are:

> *Provide one overarching goal and up to five measurable objectives. Provide specific data on the numbers served and dosage of intervention(s) if applicable.*

This is a situation in which a grant applicant is applying for funding for one part of a much larger project. As you will remember from Chapter

5, Many Churches is seeking to create a culture-changed nursing home from a traditional one. Funding from the Nale Foundation is intended only to create one prototype dining room consonant with the culture-change movement, just one small component of its overall goal.

Goal

The overarching goal is to improve the quality of life for 36 residents of Many Churches by renovating existing space within their nursing home unit to create three small, intimate dining spaces in keeping with culture-change processes to serve as models for future facility-wide changes. (Note that this goal is only one part of a major facility-wide project on culture change to affect the present 200 residents and all future residents. Matching funds are available for other components.)

Measurable Objectives

1. To educate a committee of 25 staff working with residents from that unit and our board member with expertise in contracting on what is needed to create a dining room environment consonant with the culture-change movement using content from *Promising Practices in Dining: Dignified Dining Tools and Resources* (from Pioneer Network, 2015: http://www.pioneernetwork.net/Providers/Dining/DiningTools/) via one 6-hour training session.

2. To complete plans for three kitchen and dining areas that create the look and feeling of home, using the space of three bedrooms, corridor spaces, and three meetings rooms.

3. To hire a contractor and kitchen designer for the kitchen and dining area renovations after a comprehensive bidding process.

4. To complete the renovation on budget and within the 18-month period of the grant proposal.

5. To evaluate the impact on the 36 residents via pre-and posttest of life satisfaction using established and validated measures and using these findings to guide replication on other units.

CHAPTER CHECKLIST

☐ Do you have an appealing and clear goal that states the overall purpose of your proposal?

☐ Are your objectives specific, measurable, and achievable?

☐ Are your goals written to address the needs of a population or a community, not the needs of your own agency?

☐ If appropriate, did you mirror some of the stated goals and objectives in the RFP in your own goals and objectives?

CHAPTER 10

EVALUATION AND LOGIC MODELS

CHAPTER OVERVIEW

In this chapter, you will learn:

- The definition and nature of different types of evaluations

- How to decide who is going to conduct your evaluation—internal or external evaluators?

- The differences between quantitative and qualitative data-collection methods

- Very basic statistical concepts to help an applicant without a statistical background understand some evaluation principles

- The different levels of outcome evaluations

- The definition of logic models and how are they useful in developing your proposal

- The basic components of a logic model and its relationship to the evaluation

- The steps in constructing a logic model

Introduction

This chapter contains elementary information on evaluation and logic models. Because this is a book on grant writing and not on evaluation, it is quite simplified and not in any way to be perceived as a formal introduction to statistics. If you have had a course or two in evaluation, feel free to skim this chapter. For the rest of you, this chapter is intended to provide just enough information for you to understand what a professional evaluator needs to do. This should help you to be far more comfortable when discussing your evaluation with an evaluation specialist. And, finally, after reading this chapter, you should be able write a very basic evaluation if you opt to do one internally.

Evaluations

There are three reasons for doing an evaluation. First, it is a required part of most grant applications. Second, every funder, whether it is a private foundation or a government agency, wants to know if your project worked. Did you meet the goals and objectives of the project that you submitted in your proposal? If you did not reach one or more of your goals, what went wrong? In short, they want to know if their investment improved the lives of those you serve, and if it didn't, what can be learned from what went awry. Third, you should know exactly how well your grant accomplished its goals.

Let's look at the evaluation from the funder's perspective. According to Frumkin (1999), there are five dimensions of the "philanthropic impact" that funders are looking for in an evaluation:

1. Adding to knowledge. Even if your funded program fails to meet the objective of improving lives, your findings can still help others and influence public policy. Sometimes knowing that a project approach does not work can be very useful, because the next project can build upon what you learned.

2. Improving and enriching the lives of clients.

3. Building organizational capacity. Completing a project can have a positive impact on both your staff and the structure of your organization. Funders are interested in having these outcomes documented in your evaluation.

4. Creating social capital. Grants can have the effect of crossing the boundaries of other programs and building strong communities.

5. Expressing private values and interests. Foundations are supported by donors, and many funders will expect your evaluation to demonstrate how your project met the goals, interests, and values of their donors.

Question: Should your existing staff conduct your evaluation (internal evaluation), or should you hire an outside consultant to carry out these tasks (external evaluation)? How do you decide which approach will work for you? There are positives and negatives to both approaches; here are some questions to help you decide.

Supporting an internal evaluation:

1. You have a person on your staff with grant or program evaluation experience who has credentials that a funder will respect, and that person has extra time to devote to an evaluation.

2. This staff member knows the project and the logistical issues of gathering data within your organization.

3. Your staff may resent an outsider.

4. An internal evaluation is usually far less expensive.

Supporting an external evaluation:

1. Your grant is large enough to devote 5–10% of your budget to hire an outside evaluator who will impress the funder with his or her expertise.

2. Your project is of such complexity that you need a research consultant to complete the task.

3. An external evaluator will appear to be more objective than an internal evaluator. This is critically important in a project with research implications.

4. Having an academic or research institute linkage offers you a valuable partnership that may reap many rewards:

a. Academics bring their expertise and experience in the field of evaluation.

b. They also may provide students who can assist in the evaluation, which will, hopefully, hold down the costs of the evaluation.

c. By entering into an agreement with an academic institution, you are bringing in a partner who will strengthen your proposal in the eyes of most reviewers. Further, you are creating a collaboration that may last beyond the scope of the grant.

However, if you partner with an academic institution, one issue must be confronted from the beginning: Who will control the data in terms of dissemination and publication? You will need a clearly written agreement stating that your agency "owns and controls" all of the data gathered during the evaluation process. This is especially true of the health care field, in which the personal and medical data of clients cannot be revealed publicly, and it holds true for other projects as well. You want to be the entity controlling reports about your project, although you cannot *ever* interfere with the findings.

In all likelihood, it will be to your advantage to use the expertise of the academic evaluator to bring your results to a wider audience through presentations at professional conferences and in publications. However, all of these activities should be completed on your terms. They should only go forward with your complete approval and with full credit to both your agency and the funder.

Types of Evaluations and Timing

There are many types of evaluations, but it makes sense to start with the most basic definitions: The distinction between a *formative* evaluation (also called a process evaluation) and a *summative* evaluation (also called an outcome evaluation.)

Simply put, a formative evaluation looks only at how well you conducted the grant. For example:

1. Did you or did you not engage the 100 older people in the project, as you said you would? If not, how close did you get, or did you exceed your goal?

2. Did you or did you not complete a training manual for the project, and does the manual contain the information expected in approximately the expected length? If not, why not?

The formative evaluation is not concerned with the outcome of the engagement of the older people in your project or the success of the training manual in delivering knowledge. Rather it assesses how well you accomplished the specific tasks listed in your proposal. It is also an ongoing evaluation, done as you work on the project. If you find problems early on through the formative evaluation, you can make corrections.

By contrast, a summative evaluation looks at the impact of your process activities, that is, did you obtain the results you intended as described in your objectives? For example:

1. If your goal was to reduce the rate of falls of 100 older adults by 5%, what rate of fall reduction did you actually achieve? Did you meet or exceed this goal?

2. If your goal was to reduce depression among nursing home residents, to what extent was this goal met using a standard pre- and posttest metric?

Further, both kinds of evaluation are done more than once. For a short grant, it is done typically about halfway through the grant. For a multi-year grant, it is done typically at quarterly or biyearly intervals. The interim evaluation(s) alert you as to how the project is going, and thus you can see if any changes in design are needed to meet the goals by the end of the project. Keep in mind, particularly for the process evaluation, that you are conducting this evaluation for your agency as well as for the funder. As the project moves forward, are you meeting the benchmarks you have set for yourself? Are you not only following the timeline but also meeting the goals and achieving the objectives you were funded to achieve?

Developing an Evaluation Plan

Not all grant proposals require an extensive evaluation plan. As a general rule, the larger the funder, the more likely you are to be required to prepare an elaborate evaluation plan.

The evaluation plan can be broken down into a series of steps:

1. **Define goals.** Develop a clear model of the project and identify all the key evaluation points.

2. **Break the objectives of the project into measurable outcomes.** What data do you need to collect to evaluate your objectives?

3. **Determine your schedule and timing.** If you collect data, you are obligated to report it, so make sure you are not overwhelmed with mounds of evaluation data at the end of your project. On the other hand, you want to make sure that you collect all the data you need. So, you need to find a balance between collecting all the data you might need and what you actually will need to evaluate the effectiveness of your project. Pre-planning and pre-consideration are crucial, given that you cannot go back and later collect baseline (data collected before the project starts) at a later time.

Therefore, one of the dilemmas a grant writer preparing an evaluation must face is how much data to collect. On the one hand, if you do not have a complete baseline of data, you cannot use outcome data (i.e., data gathered after the project is complete) because you have nothing to compare it with. On the other hand, over-collection of data will drown the project and annoy clients and staff. Remember to look at your goals and objectives, and be sure that the data you plan to collect will help you determine if your goals are met or not. Anything less is not enough. More than that is overkill.

4. Decide on your design. Just because focus groups may be popular at the time you write your proposal does not mean that you should use focus groups: The type of your evaluation should relate to your project. Know how you will analyze your data, considering that you may need to present these data to all interested audiences. Will you be able to summarize your data for a lay audience?

Types of Data to Be Collected

There are two general types of data: quantitative and qualitative.

Quantitative data. Anything that can be expressed as a number is considered to be quantitative data. An example would be the number of participants who completed your fall-prevention program. Quantitative data also include all the basic demographic information about your participants, including age, gender, and medical conditions. Some common sources of quantitative data are:

- Existing client records.

- Surveys with closed-end or fixed-choice questions. The most common types of closed-end/fixed-choice questions are the familiar true/false and multiple-choice types.

- Assessments, including needs assessments (see Kaufman & Guerra-Lopez, 2013; McKillip, 1987) and satisfaction surveys (see Albert & Logsdon, 2000).

- Consumer satisfaction surveys (see Cohen-Mansfield, Ejaz, & Werner, 2000).

Qualitative data. These are data that cannot be expressed as numbers but must be, in some way, analyzed and interpreted. Examples of qualitative data include open-ended survey questions and data gathered from observations. Common sources of qualitative data include:

- Observations (see Wolcott, 2008).

- Focus groups (see Krueger & Casey, 2014).

- Interviews, which may consist of both closed and open questions. They may be conducted in person, over the telephone, or, quite commonly today, by means of an Internet survey tool (see Roulston, 2010).

- Surveys with open-ended questions. For example, "What do you feel are the three greatest problems facing older people in the United States today?" (see Rea & Parker, 2014).

Note: Gathering either quantitative or qualitative data may require informed consent from the people being studied. Informed consent refers to a formal procedure to ensure that all your participants are made aware of the possible costs and risks they may encounter as a result of being part of your project. Please see Chapter 17, "Processes to Follow Postfunding," for more information on other requirements for research involving individuals.

Three Types of Research Designs

1. One-shot case studies. This is where a single group is studied only once. A group is introduced to some treatment, such as participating in a fall-prevention program, and then we look for changes in the participants. From a scientific perspective, this is the weakest research design, and it is very difficult to make any generalizations about the findings as how they would apply beyond this one single case study. It is not recommended for most grants.

2. One-group pre- and posttest design. In this design, there is a pretest of the group, there is some type of treatment, and there is a posttest evaluation to see if changes have occurred. Staying with our fall-prevention example, prior to beginning the fall-prevention program, the participants would be tested using a variety of appropriate measures (walking gait, balance, fear of falling, etc.). They would next participate in the fall-prevention program, followed by a new evaluation to see if changes had occurred. Again, as with the one-shot case study, there are numerous factors that can jeopardize the validity of your findings with this approach.

3. Two-group designs. For almost all evaluations of programs in aging service organizations, these groups are called *intervention* and *comparison groups*. For medical science research, the terms are *experimental* and *control groups*, which require far more effort to ensure that the groups are matched exactly.

> Intervention and comparison groups are used when you are testing the efficacy of an intervention (the terms for the project activity). The intervention group would receive the training and the comparison group would not (although it might participate in the intervention after the evaluation is done).

Experimental and Quasi-Experimental Designs

> In an experimental design, which are usually conducted under laboratory or highly controlled situations, your subjects are randomly assigned to groups for different levels of treatment. That is, one group receives a treatment (a drug, some form of behavioral therapy, etc.), while the control group receives either a placebo or no treatment at all. Subjects are randomly assigned to each group, and therefore each group can be considered the same.

> In a quasi-experimental research design, subjects are not randomly assigned to control groups and treatment groups, but they are reasonably expected to be very similar. In sum, in the true experimental design, there is a random assignment of subjects, while in the quasi-experimental design, there is no randomization.

In most studies in aging, such as creating, implementing, and evaluating the impact of a fall-prevention program on older adults, the research design will be quasi-experimental. Most of us do not have the luxury of taking older adults into a highly controlled laboratory setting. Our studies are conducted in senior centers, independent living apartment complexes, nursing homes, and community locations such as a YWCA. Therefore, almost all of the program evaluations in aging services will use the terms "treatment or intervention group" for participants in the project and "comparison group" for those who are not participating and to which the treatment group is compared. In the fall-prevention example, the comparison group would be used for data-collection purposes, but would not participate in the fall-prevention program (which is the intervention). The intervention group would participate in the project and would have the same data collected.

If you are doing a study that requires you to create treatment and control groups, as well as the appropriate evaluation protocols, you should be familiar with the work of Campbell and Stanley (1963). Although Campbell and Stanley first published their work 50 years ago, and much has changed since that time, they clearly outlined the differences between doing social research outside a laboratory and conducting experiments in the highly controlled environment of a laboratory. They discussed the three most common types of studies, which are still conducted today in the field of aging. In particular, they listed a number of factors that can jeopardize the validity of your project (Campbell & Stanley, 1963, pp. 5–6). Even given these drawbacks, the studies described here can provide useful data that can result in improving the quality of life of older adults.

The table below illustrates this basic design we have just described using a falls prevention program as the treatment example:

Illustration of a Quasi-Experimental Intervention/Comparison Group Design

GROUP TYPE	TIME 1	TIME 2 (INTERVENTION)	TIME 3 (MAY BE REPEATED)
Comparison	Group is evaluated.	No fall-prevention program	Evaluated for change
Treatment	Group is evaluated.	Fall-prevention program	Evaluated for change

Even using the model in the above table, there are still problems that can jeopardize the validity of the data. However, there are fewer problems than in the other designs, and as a result, this is a common way to evaluate the effectiveness of a program or service in aging.

You might ask, "Why are the two groups needed?" The anecdote in the "Sharing What We Have Learned" box explains why.

SHARING WHAT WE HAVE LEARNED

Let's consider a research project on peer mentoring of certified nursing assistants (CNAs) in nursing homes conducted by one of the authors (Hegeman, 2003). After the intervention, in which new CNAs were mentored by experienced and specially trained CNAs, the retention rate of new CNAs increased. However, at the time the study was conducted, there was a downturn in the economy and fewer CNAs were leaving their work. Without data on retention rates of both an intervention and a comparison group, one could argue that the improvement had nothing to do with the peer mentoring program and everything to do with the downturn in the economy.

Since the study had data on both a comparison group of CNAs (similar CNAs from the same nursing homes in the study but who did not take the training) as well as from the intervention group of CNAs from the same nursing homes (those who did take the training), we were able to show that while the retention rates in both groups increased and that the rate of retention was higher in the intervention group. The difference between the two groups was statistically significant, which means that we could draw the conclusion that the improvement in retention rates was due to the peer mentoring training and not the other things in the environment of the study, in this case the downturn in

> the economy. Without the data from the comparison group, we would have not been able to say with assurance that peer mentoring made a difference in retention. One could have well argued that the change was simply a result of the downturn in the economy and that the mentoring program may or may not have had an effect on retention.

The type of data analysis you do will depend, in part, on the requirements of your funder. But, it will also depend upon the type of project you are proposing. Unless you are familiar with statistical methods and have access to a data analysis program such as SPSS (McCormick & Salcedo, 2015), we strongly recommend that if your evaluation requires this level of complexity, you should work with an academic institution or other data analysis specialists.

Logic Models

What Are Logic Models and How Are They Useful in Developing Your Proposal?

When the authors began to write grant proposals early in their careers, logic models were not on anyone's radar. As we moved into the 1990s, more and more funders began to require these graphic displays. It is now rare to see an RFP for a large-scale grant that does not require some form of a logic model, because they serve as a way to (a) communicate your ideas more effectively to your partners and stakeholders and (b) help you design your proposal.

We are also now seeing another model used: theory of change. Although in many cases these models are being used interchangeably, they are not really the same. While this section will focus on logic models, we will also distinguish between the concepts of logic models and theory of change models.

Definitions

Logic models are sometimes referred to as outcome models. They are designed to graphically depict the components of your proposed program and to clarify the inputs, activities, and outcomes for you, your staff, stakeholders, and, of course, your funder. The most common form of logic model in use today is usually called the basic United Way format (Clark & Anderson, 2004; United Way of America, 1996). The format we use here has been modified to include the impacts of your proposed activity. While an Internet search will yield a number of variations, all logic models reflect these basic components.

Logic Model: First Approach

Inputs	Activities	Outputs	Short-Term Outcomes	Long-Term Outcomes	Impacts

Once you have identified the items that fall under each of these components, the next thing is to identify the indicators for each, including definitions and specifications of how each will be measured.

Logic Model Template with Indicators

	Inputs	Activities	Outputs	Short-Term Outcomes	Long-Term Outcomes	Impacts
Logic Model						
Indicators						

Theories of change are developed to link activities and outcomes to explain both how and why the expected change will develop. The purpose of a theory of change is not only to convey the purpose and direction of your project, but also to show the relationships between multiple factors that will have an influence on your outcomes. The approach is also designed to identify all the factors and interventions that may influence these outcomes.

Theory of Change Model: Hospital-to-Home Care Transitions

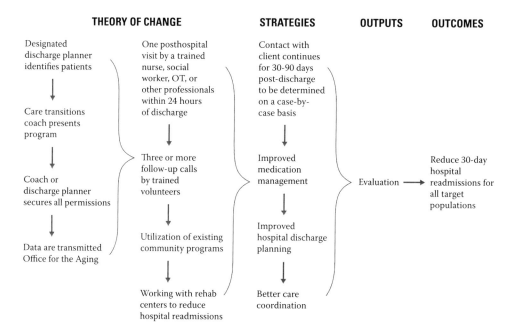

The theory of change model above was developed for an Area Agency on Aging (AAA) by one of the authors. The format of theory of change is not as standardized as logic models. This approach links outcomes and activities to explain how the change outlined in your proposal is expected to come about. For more discussion of theory of change and logic models consult Clark and Anderson (2004).

The Steps in Building a Logic Model

A logic model should be developed at the beginning of the development of the proposal. The model will need to undergo changes and modifications as the proposal is developed. Here are some key steps in creating putting together a logic model:

- Start early. As your project emerges, build your logic model. A logic model will allow to see if all the components of your project fit together.

- Involve your proposal team (if the grant is large enough to warrant one) in the development of the model. Not everyone will "start in the same place"; the logic model will alert you to those knowledge gaps.

- Take good notes as you develop your model. It is important to remember what you considered and why something was not included in the model.

- Tie the construction of your logic model into the timeline for development of your proposal.

- Strike a balance between simplicity and detail in the model. While this is a general recommendation, some suggest that you make the first draft very detailed and edit down until you have a concise and clear model.

- There are two basic strategies for developing a logic model. In a forward-looking model, you start with inputs and build the model forward following the projected path of the grant. In a backward-looking model, you begin with the outcomes (or impacts) and work backward, asking the question, "How do I accomplish this?" Many find that it is not an either/or approach but that you will look both forward and backward.

- When you look at your first draft, the question you have to ask is, "Does this make sense to someone who is unfamiliar with the proposal?"

- Once funded, you will want to revisit your logic model and make changes during the implementation phase.

When completed, your logic model should present a clear picture of how your proposal will work. What inputs will you need (staff, equipment, etc.)? What are the key activities involved in the proposal (training key staff, recruiting volunteers, developing materials, etc.)? What are the outputs and short- and long-term outcomes? What will be the impact on your clients, agency, and/or community?

A logic model brings everyone together so they are able to clearly state the goals and objectives of the project. A logic model provides a useful tool for communicating your project to not only your staff, partners, and stakeholders but also to the public, including legislators and other government officials.

Illustrative Evaluation Section

As you will remember from Chapter 5 ("Three Fictitious Organizations Serving the Aging"), The Nale City Multiservice Senior Center is seeking a grant to develop a fall-prevention program.

The specific requirements of the Nale Foundation for writing the evaluation, as stated in the requirements for writing the narrative, are:

> What is your process for evaluating success in achieving your organization's (or your program's) goals?

However, in the criteria section, the request for proposal (RFP) also states that it expects to see a quasi-experimental design used in the evaluation. Note that since the money available for this grant is so modest, it will be almost impossible to do an elaborate quasi-experimental design.

As you will remember, this fictitious RFP set the applicants many challenges. The disparity between the level of funding and the grant requirements is one of them. In real life, if you find that you cannot possibly accomplish the elements requested given the budget, you should try to work creatively to resolve the disconnect as much as possible.

In the illustrative evaluation shown, the fiscal problem was resolved because the Nale City Multiservice Senior Center recruited a college student intern who is doing the evaluation as part of a field placement. Here is the illustrative example:

We will evaluate the impact of Stop Falls Now (SFN) by a using a somewhat quasi-experimental design in which we compare the rate of falls between elders taking the program with people in the senior center who are not taking the program. To the extent possible, we will match the groups in terms of age, gender, ethnicity, and self-reported assessment of health.

Measures will be gathered at baseline (Month 3 of project before any training) and at 1-, 3-, and 6-month intervals after training is completed by a college intern. Using the SPSS data analysis, the intern will apply appropriate statistical tests to compare the differences between the two groups. We will define success as a statistically different rate of falls between the two groups, with the intervention group having the significantly lower rate.

We acknowledge that there are some threats (Note: the term "threats" is commonly used in an evaluation discussion to describe shortcomings in the evaluation design that might make results questionable). However, given the funding limit, it is a reasonable approach to use. Threats include the small size of the sample (it may be hard to achieve significance) and the possibility that the two groups will not be a match. It is unknown, since the intervention group is self-selected, whether they are more or less likely to fall than the comparison group, and therefore findings may be questioned.

For participants only, we will also do satisfaction survey at the end of the training, so improvements can be made in the next waves of training.

CHAPTER CHECKLIST

☐ Have you decided what type of evaluation you will use?

☐ Have you decided who is going to conduct the evaluation?

☐ Do you have a clear understanding of the data-collection methods?

☐ Have you developed a logic model, even if it is not required to be submitted with your proposal?

☐ Have you used the basic components of your logic model to demonstrate the relationships between your evaluation methods and your outcomes?

CHAPTER 11

BUILDING A LOGICAL WORK PLAN (METHODOLOGY)
AND TIMELINE

CHAPTER OVERVIEW

In this chapter, you will learn about:

- Definitions of timelines and work plans (sometimes called the methodology)

- How to write the work plan so it is appealing to reviewers while also meeting the needs of the organization

- How and why to get critical feedback from the staff about the work plan

- How to use your timeline and goals and objectives as an organizing tool for the work plan section

- Common errors to avoid when writing this section

- How to use the timeline as the basis for a realistic budget (a very clever grant-writing tip)

- Other tips on writing this section of your grant

What Is a Timeline?

The timeline (required in most, but not all, grants) is a sequential table of the tasks in your work plan. It sequentially lists each task, the time frame for each task, and the people needed to complete the task in a chart form. Most timelines will look like the chart below (although they may vary from grant application to grant application) and sometimes have to be in a narrative format to fit into an online application.

TIME FRAME	TASK	STAFF RESPONSIBLE

(Your table will usually have far more horizontal lines than this one.)

As always, follow the instructions in the request for proposal (RFP). Sometimes funders want to see additional columns in the timeline or will have the columns in a different order. For example, applications for large governmental grants sometimes have a more complex timeline with categories like this:

OBJECTIVES	ACTIVITIES	RESPONSIBLE PERSON	COMPLETION DATE	TRACKING/ EVALUATION METHODS

As you can imagine, by the time you have a completed a timeline of this nature, you will have basically outlined your work plan and your evaluation section. Indeed, when this kind of comprehensive timeline is requested, the RFP does not always require a separate work plan.

What Is a Work Plan?

The work plan is your blueprint of operations. It explains *how, when, and with whom* you will complete the proposal. Unlike the timeline, it may not necessarily be sequential, but rather organized by type of activity. **In your work plan, you not only list the items to be accomplished but also explain how they will be accomplished.**

Our approach, when using the simpler timeline more commonly found, is to think of the work plan as the narrative version of the timeline. For example, if an agency were to use volunteers in its program, the timeline for this item might look like this:

TIME FRAME	TASK	STAFF RESPONSIBLE
Months 1–2	Recruit 20 volunteers	Project manager

The section of the work plan related to this task would include sentences with information that answers the following questions:

- What kinds of volunteers will be recruited (skilled or not)?

- How will they be recruited?

- Who will recruit them?

- What are the requirements for volunteers in terms of education, experience, background checks, immunizations, and so on?

- How will you handle any barriers to recruitment?

- How will you ensure diversity among your volunteers (for most grants)?

- What is your plan for the management and supervision of the volunteers?

As you write this section, remember the multiple roles you have as a grant writer (see Chapter 3, "Conceptualizing the Multiple Roles of a

Grant Writer for Aging Services"). For the work plan section, you are not only answering the questions in the RFP but also working as a marketer to showcase your managerial acumen by accurately predicting and explaining the needed activities of the project. Be sure that your project sounds professional and well thought out.

You must consider the reviewers. You need to accommodate two potentially different kinds of reviewers: those who are not familiar with your field and those who are. The first type of reviewer might not know the common assumptions of people who work in your field. Therefore, be as jargon-free as possible; for example, write "help home care clients walk" rather than "increase ambulation of the clients." The second kind of reviewer may know your field extremely well and will be looking to see if you covered all of the bases. For example, in a grant that focuses on using volunteers to enrich the lives of elders, a reviewer might be a current or former health care manager and will downgrade your proposal if you do not state that you will provide the required immunizations and background checks for volunteers.

Differences Between the Timeline and the Work Plan

The timeline, as noted above, is chronological. In the work plan, all related activities are usually in one section even if they are not in the same time frame. For example, the timeline would list the tasks associated with an evaluation in different rows, with the pretests done early in the project, posttests toward the end, and a final report at the very end. By contrast, when developing the section of the work plan devoted to the evaluation, all evaluation activities would be described there.

Depending on the length and complexity of the proposal (which in turn is guided by limitations in the RFP), the work plan section may be just a page or two or many pages long. Some items might not appear in the timeline for reasons of space, but would have to be added to the work plan. Now that we have a good working definition of the timeline and the work plan, let's move on to the steps in constructing this section:

1. Consult With the Staff Members Who Will Manage the Grant and Other Stakeholders When Developing the Timeline and the Work Plan

This consultation is needed because you will learn about issues and challenges in running the project that you may not have considered. One of the themes running throughout this book is that the grant writer should not be the only one planning the proposal. This theme is especially important for the timeline and methodology sections.

In a natural eagerness to get the work plan written in a way that will be appealing to funders, grant writers sometimes forget that the work plan must actually work in real life for the aging service organization. The people who will run and manage the grant or who receive services from the grant will have a far better idea of what is needed to make a project work well on a day-to-day level than will a grant writer or CEO. While input from these stakeholders is critical, grant writers should also respect their time when seeking their input. Engage them wisely. We suggest sending them your draft timeline, with a note saying you must have missed something and request that they join you for a brief meeting to help you complete it. Alternatively, they can email suggestions, but the chance to bounce ideas off each other can be lost.

Alas, almost everyone is far better at identifying problems (and complaining bitterly about them afterwards) than they are at solving them. So, expect a litany of complaints about how difficult the project will be. The challenge for the grant writer is to elicit solutions to the challenges, perhaps by first thanking stakeholders for their useful information on the problems and then asking, "Given your expertise, what do you see as creative ways to work around the problem?" "What resources could the grant provide to address them?"

Here is an example of effective use of staff input from the Friends and Neighbors Home Health Care Agency.

SCENARIO

For a training program on good communication among staff, clients, and family members, the grant writer began to develop the work plan by consulting with staff to predict operational challenges. Staff members noted two major obstacles: (a) Where would they get replacement staff to care for the frail and sick people they serve when some direct care staff were being trained in the communication program? (b) How would they cover the extra costs of replacement staff, as well as the regular staff being trained, with a tight budget?

The grant writer thanked the staff for their insights. By asking the right questions, the grant writer engaged the staff to help develop solutions to problems that needed to be included: (a) offer part-time workers additional hours so they could cover the caseload of the staff being trained and (b) request dollars in the grant budget for these additional personnel costs.

Such logistical solutions are covered in the work plan as space allows. For example, to address the obstacle described above, the work plan would include sentences like, "Our scheduler will develop alternative working hours so that those staff who attend training will be replaced by other staff, who in turn will be trained in a later iteration of training. Time spent in training will be reimbursed at the regular rate." See the exemplar at the end of this chapter, and remember that a discussion of the costs of the work is not provided in the work plan. Rather, that goes into the budget section.

2. Write This Section: A Suggested Process

a. Prepare a draft timeline first. This should be done even if you have a potential funder that does not require one. Why? It can serve as an organizational tool, like an outline, for the work plan, and it helps you to organize your thoughts. Like your planning abstract (see Chapter 2, "Pre-Planning Your Grant Proposal: Modules and Sharing Your Grant Concept to Get Critical Feedback and Support"), the draft timeline should change as your management design becomes clearer.

b. Use the timeline as the first part of your work plan narrative if the grant guidelines allow this option (some specify, for example, that a timeline be a separate appendix). If it is an option, a timeline in front of the work plan will give the reviewer a welcome overview of what to expect in the rest of the section.

c. Keep your draft timeline next to you as you write the work plan. You may find that you omitted necessary steps that need to be added to the timeline.

d. Keep a logical flow from the goals and objectives section to this section. Consider using phrasing such as:

> To achieve Objective 1 (___repeat the objective if
> space allows) _____), we have _____ steps.

Then describe how the steps in the work plan relate to the objective and continue on in that manner with the different objectives.

Note: This phrasing will work in many grant applications, but not all. If it seems awkward or contrived in the context of an individual proposal, it should be omitted, particularly if the narrative is short in length.

e. Use this clever trick: Add a temporary column called "Notes on Related Costs" to a temporary timeline that is for your use only. This added column will *never* appear in the timeline you submit in the grant (unless of course the funder asks for it). It is for your writing and subsequent budgeting use only. It is very effective to use this temporary column while you are preparing the work plan section, as it is at that point that you are most likely to see the costs related to each task. Without it, it is very easy to miss costs when you are preparing the budget.

f. Let's be clear: You are not creating this temporary additional column table to help you with the work plan. Rather, it will help you *later* when you write your budget when you can refer back to it. Without it, you are not likely to remember all operational costs, See below for a sample.

Here is a sample temporary timeline (not complete as it is provided for illustration only) for the Friends and Neighbors Home Health Care Agency, which is seeking funds to provide training for its staff on effective communication techniques with challenging clients (especially those with dementia) and their families. (Remember that the fourth column in the timeline is for your temporary use and will not be included in the grant proposal.)

SAMPLE TEMPORARY TIMELINE FOR THE GRANT WRITER'S USE ONLY			
Time Frame (in months)	**Task**	**Staff**	**Temporary Column** *Notes on costs* *(To be used later when writing budget but not included in the timeline you submit)*
1	Staff planning team meets to review grant requirements and determine recruitment and training logistics.	PD PC E T	Staff time (estimate hours), consulting fees for evaluator and trainer
1	Recruitment materials mailed, emailed, or hand-delivered.		Staff time (estimate hours), mailing costs of recruitment flyer to clients, costs of printing recruitment flyer
2	Selected staff informed of training dates and arrangements made for replacement staff during first of two trainings.	PD SC	Staff time for rescheduling staff (estimate hours), costs of replacement staff when staff are being trained (Note to self: Additional transportation reimbursement to training staff)
Key: PD = project director, PC = members of the planning committee, SC = schedule coordinator, T = trainer, E = evaluator			

3. Answer Questions Fully

The reviewers are looking for information, in a spelled-out and logical sequence, on how the project will operate. They also want to know how well you have predicted management challenges and how they might be addressed.

SHARING WHAT WE HAVE LEARNED

One of us recently reviewed a proposal to a governmental entity. The RFP stated that the applicant should explain how training would be designed and evaluated. In the work plan, the applicant only wrote, "We have a comprehensive training and evaluation plan conducted by experts," and then described the qualifications of these experts in detail.

This work plan received a low score because the applicant did not include any information at all about the design of the training or how the training would be evaluated. The applicant seemed to assume that having expert trainers and evaluators was all that was needed. **Wrong!**

The reviewers could not make a determination about the quality of the training, the amount of the training (the "dosage"), or its evaluation just because "experts" would be involved, and so the grade on this section of the proposal was very low. Having experts was an asset, of course, but not describing what the experts would create was a major weakness. Watch out for errors of this kind and answer each category fully.

While it could be that a project task is to develop the content of the training, the applicant could have written something like this: Our expert consultants will review three evidence-based programs in this general area (listing them) and then combine them to make one program tailored to a senior population, including cultural modifications for our primarily _____ (name ethnic groups) population. We anticipate offering the program for 1 hour once a week for 12 weeks and repeating the training cycle three times a year. Our evaluation consultant will use a pre- and posttest format to determine knowledge gain and will give the same tests to a comparison group of similar elders not in the program.

Illustrative Work Plan Narrative

The Friends and Neighbors Home Health Care Agency (Friends and Neighbors) is seeking a grant to improve communication between staff and family members by using an evidence-based training program in this area. The specific requirements of the Nale Foundation for writing the work plan are very simple: *Explain your project in detail.*

Because the work plan is so long, we have provided only the first three items in the work plan as exemplars.

First Three Steps in the Work Plan

1. Hold a staff, family, and consultant planning meeting early in Month 1 to review the grant activities. The executive director, the nurse educator, two nurses, two aides, two family members, and the training and evaluation consultants will attend. The agenda is to (a) review the entire project; (b) learn how the training and evaluation will be structured for both staff and family members; (c) discuss any anticipated implementation issues and possible solutions; (d) review timelines for recruitment, training, and evaluation and review expectations for each member of the team; and (e) discuss the content of the recruitment flyer and decide on recruitment strategies.

2. Recruit family members to participate in a separate family training, one held during the day and one at night to accommodate working family members. Training will be held in a donated community hall next to our offices. The recruitment flyer will provide information on a special 2-hour companion service (at a special rate) we will offer for the evening of the training so family members of clients who need constant supervision can attend. Recruitment involves (a) hand-delivered flyers to the family members who live with the client, (b) email, twitter and text (as appropriate for the audience), (c) traditional mail, and (d) follow-up telephone calls to family members who have not responded.

3. Create an efficient schedule for staff to attend. The staff scheduler will set five varied training dates and times for our 100 nurses, aides, and home companions. The varied time is intended to accommodate the busy schedules of staff. Everyone will be paid at his or her usual hourly rate for the additional time in training as no overtime is anticipated. When the training time requires that replacement staff cover their usual home visits, the scheduler will arrange for this coverage as well. Training will be held at a donated community space near our office.

CHAPTER CHECKLIST

☐ Have you engaged appropriate staff (i.e., those who will work on the grant or be affected by it) and family members in the development of the work plan? Have you addressed any implementation concerns they may have?

☐ Have you created a working draft timeline to help you organize the narrative for the methodology? Will you remember to revise it as you work?

☐ Have you created a temporary column in the draft timeline to note the costs that will be associated with each activity? Be sure to remove it from the version you submit.

☐ Did you answer all of the questions in this section fully?

☐ When you read this section over, did you check to see that you had addressed any problems in the application that a reviewer might see?

CHAPTER 12

DEVISING A FUNCTIONAL AND ACCURATE BUDGET

CHAPTER OVERVIEW

In this chapter, you will find information about:

- How the budget evolves directly from the work plan and the input of the staff involved

- The dangers of poor budgeting

- How to determine the amount of the grant award and whether or not it makes sense to apply given early projected costs

- Common expense and income categories

- How to understand indirect costs, matching funds, and in-kind requirements

- How to address an ethical dilemma: Should you ask for the highest amount possible even when it exceeds your needs?

- A checklist for reviewing your budget

Introduction: Your Budget and Your Work Plan

A budget is not a simple division of the amount of money in the grant, nor is it an afterthought. It is a key component of your proposal! You need to begin to form your budget as your proposal begins to take shape. It is the budget that lets you know if your project is feasible. If you wait until the last minute to draft your budget, you may find that the proposal you have worked on so diligently will not work out financially. Therefore, it is critical to engage your financial staff early on in the process.

As you will remember from the previous chapter, your budget evolves directly from your work plan. Specifically, we suggested adding and saving a temporary column to your timeline in which you note related costs. This temporary column captures costs that you can now include in your budget.

Important to Note

1. Remember, once your grant proposal is in its final stages, changes in your goals, work plan, deliverables, and/or the total amount of funding must be made to reflect budgetary changes. It is very common to find that once you have a detailed budget prepared, you need to pare down activities or the number of people involved to stay within the budget.

2. Every funder has different rules regarding how you prepare the budget. Follow the guidelines in the grant application rather than what is written here. Remember that the grantor is your customer.

3. Some funders provide very clear and detailed information on how to create a budget. Take advantage of this information if it is available to you.

4. Every funder will have a slightly different budget format and requirements. So, read the instructions carefully. For some large grants, there are conference calls and webinars to prepare you to write a complete proposal. Take advantage of any of these invaluable services to learn in more detail what budget expectations are.

CASE STUDY: THE DANGER OF POOR BUDGET PLANNING

An Area Agency on Aging (AAA) applied for a grant to expand its home-delivered meals program. The grant was carefully crafted to expand the program into some of the most hard-to-reach rural counties in the region. Grant funding would cover two new kitchen facilities to allow for local meal distribution. The budget also included funding for one additional staff person to conduct outreach to reach new participants and bring in new volunteers.

The proposal was fully funded for 3 years. Once the grant was awarded, the finance office made a startling discovery. The home-delivered meals program budget lacked a budget line to cover one crucial expense, the cost of transportation! In other words, the agency did not request funding for mileage. An urgent request to the funder to alter the budget was turned down. They were told they had to meet the goals of the grant with the funding allocated. The AAA was forced to reduce other programming, not fill one open staff position, and make other budget cuts.

What Is the Amount of the Grant Award?

There are three ways funders inform you about the amount of award they will provide:

1. Some requests for proposals (RFPs) state specifically what the award amount will be. For example, the RFP might state, "There will be eight awards totaling no more than $100,000 each."

2. Some RFPs state that there is a total amount of money available but do not specify the maximum size of each grant.

3. Some smaller foundations may accept proposals without guidelines concerning the total amount available at all.

For #1, your question will be, "What are our chances of being one of the eight successful applicants?" First, you should consider the scope of the funder's range. Being one of eight from a funder who awards grants in all

50 states or internationally makes your odds very poor indeed and would not be a great option for a grant novice to consider. If, however, the funder only awards grants within one county, where there will be far fewer competitors, your chances are much better.

For #2, first check the funder's website or ask for its annual report. Either of these usually provides lists of recent awards, along with the amounts. While that information may not apply to the new grant, it gives you some idea of general funding levels. Read carefully. If there were 20 awards and 19 were in the $25,000 range and only one was for $100,000, without further information, you should not infer that you too can apply for $100,000. Your best chance would be the $25,000 range.

For #3, there are several approaches. First, in some cases, smaller foundations may be managed by a regional community foundation, and you may able to get advice by contacting that organization. Second, it has been the author's experience that some smaller foundations are looking for local projects to fund, and a phone call will provide you with a wealth of information and assistance. Third, all is not lost when none of the above approaches work. You can determine what past funding practices have been when the funder will not reveal this information by accessing and reviewing Form 990 (a federal tax filing form) of the funder. Here is the procedure:

1. Set your browser to http://foundationcenter.org/findfunders/990finder/. (Some computers will require that you first find www.foundationcenter.org. Then you can search for 990 forms.)

2. Click on Find Foundations on the top.

3. Click on 990 Finder.

4. Fill in the boxes for Fund Name and State (leave everything else blank).

5. Click Find.

6. Click on most recent fiscal year available.

7. Scroll down (a lot) to the end of the attachments and allow time for all the pages to load. You will find the listing of grant awards with the dollar amount.

Once you know the amount of the grant award or at least the past pattern of the funder, you need to ask yourself a series of budget-related questions that will help you determine whether or not to continue with the grant application:

1. Is the award big enough to cover all the costs of operating the grant?

2. Is the grant award big enough to be worth your time? Sometimes you will expend more staff time writing the grant than you will recoup with funds from the grant, and your time could be better used elsewhere.

3. How costly will the grant be to manage? For example, if a grant is only for $5,000, but it requires detailed monthly progress and financial reports, the entire project may result in a net loss for the agency.

4. Despite all of the above discussion, is there ever a case for a small grant, even one as low as $1,000? Sometimes, surprisingly, the answer is yes. Here are some reasons to consider applying for a mini-grant:

   a. You have won no grants before, and a small grant will enable you to say you have some track record with grants.

   b. The RFP is in an area of intense interest to your organization, and the organization is committed to providing this service and was looking for some partial support that it could match. In this case, the small amount of money supports what you were hoping to do, with or without funding, so a small award is better than no award.

   c. You have enough volunteers to help with the management of the grant so that staff is not overly engaged in running such a small project.

Common Income Categories

Common income categories are the expected grant award (self-explanatory), in-kind funds, matching funds, and other income.

In-Kind Funds

In-kind funds are not actually paid in cash, but rather are the value of services or products donated to the project. Funders like to see in-kind funds because they document the commitment of the applicant agency to the project and also lower the amount that the applicant requests. Some examples:

- The agency provides a project coordinator and does not request grant funds for some or all of the coordinator's salary and fringe benefits. For example, the project coordinator will work 50% on the grant, the agency will pay for 20% of the coordinator's time, and the grant budget calls for 30%. The 20% is an in-kind cost.

- The agency provides meal costs for participants or uniforms for volunteers and does not charge the grant for them.

- Volunteers' time. Look at www.independentsector.org/volunteer time to find the value of volunteer work in your state. Be sure to provide this citation when using volunteer time as an in-kind cost because the value of volunteer time is surprisingly high: In their latest report available before the completion of this book, the national average was $23.56 per hour. Be sure the use the correct dollar amount for your state.

- Donation of consultants or grant partners. For example, the usual rate of one of your consultants is $100 per hour, but this consultant will do the work for this project for $75 an hour (the in-kind funds are $25 per hour worked). In the exemplar at the end of this chapter, you will see that the time of a college intern in managing the evaluation is an in-kind cost.

- Value of indirect costs when not allowed as a project expense. (See below for definition of indirect costs.)

Matching Funds

Matching funds cover some of the project costs that will not be covered by the grant. Matching funds are donated by the agency itself or other contributors (grant partners, donors, etc.). Occasionally, another grant may be a source of matching funds. (Note: Most governmental grants do not allow matching funds from another governmental agency.) Be sure to check the guidelines of the funder to be sure what is and is not allowed as matching funds.

Both matching and in-kind funds must be documentable! Matching funds and in-kind funds are not mere window dressing to make your application look stronger. They are formal commitments of funds to your project. Therefore, you must be able to document them on request.

Because both matching and in-kind funds must be documented, there is a cost associated with them. Someone—either project staff or someone in the accounting department—must track them and keep a record of them so they are ready for audit. Therefore, consider the impact on the staff working on the project. If there is considerable matching or in-kind funds, increase the time an appropriate staff member will have to spend on the grant by a small percentage. Depending on the grant and the level of work in getting the matching funds, this amount could be as much as 3–5% in addition to the usual work on the grant.

Both of us know from bitter experience that the extra staff time needs to be covered for activities like this. When you have not planned for this staff time, a staff member will have to devote unreimbursed time to these tasks, leading to considerable frustration.

Other Income Categories

Grants differ so greatly in content that there may well be other sources of income you should consider including in your budget. These might include program fees (e.g., if teaching courses on improving the balance of elders, the agency may charge a sliding-scale fee), board-designated funds (the board may agree to provide a certain amount of money from an operating or special account to support the project), and fundraisers (staff may decide to add a fundraiser to support the specific project). Of course, since the amount of income may be hard to predict, it is best to underestimate the expected income from these income categories.

Common Expense Categories

One of the first steps in preparing your budget is to inventory all of the projected personnel- and non-personnel-related expenses. Look at any new costs specific to the grant (hiring consultants, travel, etc.) that will be incurred if your grant is funded.

The following is a list of common expenses:

- Salaries and fringe benefits (full-time equivalents [FTEs]). List each regular employee who will be involved in the grant and the percentage of time each will spend on the project.

- Consultants and temporary employees. In recent years the Internal Revenue Service (IRS) has developed a set of very strict and enforced guidelines on determining who qualifies as a consultant (independent contractor) and who is a temporary employee. For guidance, refer to IRS Topic 762—Independent Contractor vs. Employee (https://www.irs.gov/taxtopics/tc762.html).

- Conferences and meetings (attending a conference or hosting a conference).

- Equipment (there may be some restrictions for this category).

- Insurance.

- Local transportation.

Other significant expenses:

- CEOs and other executives who provide significant leadership at strategic points in the project. An accurate, small percentage of their time in this leadership role can and should be charged to the grant. Notice that we used the word *accurate*!

• Undergraduate, graduate, and postdoctoral students who have a limited involvement in the grant, such as data analysis near the end of the project. If students are an integral part of the budget, create a separate, clearly labeled budget category to cover their costs. This would go under a consultant line, rather than in the salary section. When you pay someone as a consultant, you are generally not required to pay fringe benefits. However, you may need to report their income using IRS Form 1099. Confirm this information with your accountant as rules change.

• Photocopying.

• Postage and printing.

• Rent and utilities.

• Supplies.

• Telephone.

• Travel.

• Other (see the following section about other costs).

The following are expenses that may apply to some projects:

• Advertising

• Board expenses

• Dues and subscriptions

• Program materials

Other or Project-Specific Costs

1. First, spell out expenses in this area in as much detail as possible so the funder does not question them. After all, if they are not listed in a given budget, the funder was not expecting to see them.

2. Be careful about putting too much money in this category. If you have a substantial amount of expenses in this area, consider creating one or two additional budget accounts to reduce this balance if you can change the budget format.

3. Finally, if you are not allowed to add additional expense categories to your budget, consider renaming some of your expenses. For example, you may have significant publicity costs, but find there is no line for these costs. Instead of a separate line for publicity, add costs for the paper for flyers under the supply or printing line and mailing costs for flyers under postage.

Special Costs That Relate to a Specific Project
Many proposals are written to carry out something that is innovative and, therefore, may not fit neatly into the common expense categories. Some examples might include:

- Animal costs (you are carrying out a pet therapy program in a nursing home).
- Patient care costs (these could include medical costs but also could cover such things as costs related to a fall-prevention or exercise program).
- Publication costs (one of the deliverables is a manual that will be widely disseminated or even an edited book).
- Travel to conferences to disseminate findings.

First, these kinds of costs are ideal for the renaming concept discussed above. Animal costs, for example, would fall under the supply line. Another alternative is to contract with another entity for unusual costs. Two examples:

1. You could have a separate subcontract with an animal shelter and that contract would cover all animal costs and insurances.

2. You might hire an expert in fall prevention and include the costs for training supplies into the subcontract for that expert.

What to Do If Your Budget Is Too High

Almost every grant writer will have the frustrating experience of completing the budget and finding, despite a lot of careful planning, that the total exceeds the maximum level of funding offered. If you have been careful not to delay developing your budget until the last minute, all is not lost. Here are some strategies you can consider using:

1. Shorten the time frame: If the funder allows this and the grant activities make this possible, shorten the time you would be operating the grant, for example, changing your time frame from 2 years to 20 or 22 months. The 2 to 4 months saved from salary and fringe benefits costs may bring your budget down sufficiently.

2. Decrease the number of clients to be served: If you have high costs for client activities, consider offering the program to fewer clients during the grant period or having some clients pay their own way without grant funds, using a means test.

3. Eliminate the least critical grant activity: Take out one or more components of your project. For example, (a) if your staff-training grant is using activities from two evidence-based programs, eliminate some activities from the second program or omit all components of the second program; or (b) if your grant involves enrichment activities for seniors, eliminate activities that involve travel expenses.

4. Look closely for any costs that could be covered by in-kind or matching funds.

Needless to say, the first three suggested changes will require that you rewrite most sections of your narrative, particularly the goal, objectives, and methodology. It is also possible that these budget changes may mean that some items in your needs assessment will no longer be met. Be sure that you have time to make the needed narrative changes throughout.

Understanding the Differences Between Direct and Indirect/Overhead Costs

Direct costs are those expenses that can be directly assigned to the project for which you are seeking funding. Such things as personnel, photo-copying, printing, and supplies to be used in completing the project are all examples of direct costs. You would not be incurring these costs if the grant did not exist.

Indirect costs and **overhead** are used interchangeably. They refer to costs such as telephone and utilities that are needed for the project, but also exist whether or not you are funded, and increase because you are running the grant project. For example, you do not rent new office space or set up specific telephone lines for a project, but a percentage of the costs of your space and telephone is necessary to make the project possible. These other necessary costs fall into the general category of indirect costs. It is assumed that the grant activity will generate additional indirect costs, including such things as additional cleaning supplies, utility costs, office equipment, and even an increase in cell phone and computer usage.

Most agencies have a fairly clear understanding of their direct costs. However, their grasp of indirect costs is usually less clear. Some funders, especially governmental ones, ask you to provide either an indirect cost or overhead rate or a percentage of indirect costs to direct costs. Others may provide you with a maximum indirect cost that you can add to your budget request.

If you do not already have one, your accountant would need to work with the funder to develop a documented and appropriate indirect cost rate for your agency. Guidelines for determining this rate can usually be found on the website of the funder. As a way of planning for future grants, your agency accountant should look at prospective funders to see how these rates are determined and develop one for the agency in advance.

It is increasingly common for a funder to deny any indirect costs at all or allow a fixed percentage of the grant award as the indirect cost rate. We have seen rates as low as 0% or as high as 8% in recent years.

Colleges and universities often have expense rates as high as 50% or more. If you are contracting with an educational institution, be sure that this total percentage rate is not included in their consulting fee. If they are unwilling (or unable) to agree to a contract for less than their full indirect rate, you have to decide whether this cost is worth it to you. One possible option is to hire a faculty member privately or a consultant to do the work.

Your accountant may determine that your indirect costs exceed the amount of the indirect costs allowed. If this is the case, request the maximum indirect costs allowed as a project expense and add the remainder as an in-kind contribution to the proposal.

Some Suggestions About Multiyear Budgets

We have three suggestions when preparing a multiyear budget:

1. Be aware that each year will not be symmetrical. The budget needs to account for inflation, salary increases, and anticipated raises in each year. It is critical to account for inflation, salary, and fringe benefits being reimbursed by showing the anticipated increase in the budget for each subsequent year. If not, you are incurring staff costs that are not being reimbursed. Other costs may also be prone to upward changes in future years. Be sure that each year shows these projected increases. Otherwise, there will be actual costs that you will have to absorb yourself. In addition, Year 1 may be lower than Year 2 because the first 3–6 months are devoted to planning and there are few operational costs for those months.

2. Determine during the grant preparation whether funds can carry over from one year to the next. It has been our experience that funds—happily—commonly do carry over from year to year, but you should be sure of this carry-over option. If it is not the case, you run the risk of being in an extremely difficult position, as project income may be lost because of circumstances beyond your control or your ability to predict. Be sure this is discussed with your program officer while preparing the proposal.

Ethical Dilemma 4: "Should you ask for the highest amount possible even when it exceeds your needs?" Our opinion is that you should request a reasonable amount of money to complete the project with a small amount of extra money in the staff line. We consider this ethical because you are projecting time and you may not be accurate. For example, it is hard to say whether a task will take 50% or 60% of staff time, especially when you do not know what obstacles may arise when you execute the project.

Randomly "padding" the budget is never a good idea. Even if budget analysis is not a strength of your grant's reviewers, they will use the "Does this look reasonable?" test. Based on their experience (remember that reviewers are generally grant writers themselves and/or grant managers who write or manage budgets for their own proposals), they ask themselves: "Is the amount requested too high?" If yes, it can jeopardize your proposal.

Reviewers will also ask themselves if any line items in the budget are too low. A figure that is too low may mean that you will not have enough funding to complete the objectives of the proposal, which could doom it to failure. It also may seem to the reviewer that you are too inexperienced with budgeting to run a program.

Then there is the ongoing problem of the funder who routinely awards grants at 10–30% or lower than what is asked. We wish we could tell you that this never happens, but it does! This is a real danger and may seem to justify padding a budget.

In most cases, you can work with your program officer to reduce the scope of your work to be commensurate with the amount of dollars awarded and it is the approach we prefer.

However, if you know that your funder has a past pattern of reducing funding and not allowing you to reduce program activities, the only prudent thing to do is to develop a budget that is estimated on the high side. To remain ethical, be sure you can use the additional dollar request in ways that will enhance and enrich your project.

Writing the Budget Narrative

Consider the budget as an outline and the budget narrative the text that explains the costs and, when possible, why the costs are essential. Usually there is no room in a line-item budget to explain these costs. Once in a while, however, you may encounter an RFP in which there is only a budget, with room to add a sentence or two explaining your costs.

It is critical than the budget narrative match the budget. Usually it is the applicant that creates the budget change, but sometimes it is the funder. We have seen cases when applications are re-submitted without changing anything even though the guidelines are different. It is crucial that you keep aware of what the budget is and what your deliverables are, as can be seem in the "Sharing What We Have Learned" box below.

SHARING WHAT WE HAVE LEARNED

One of the authors was hired to manage a state-funded grant for an association. The former director of the association wrote a grant in response to a state RFP with a total funding cap of $1,000,000. The project was removed from the final state budget, but the idea was carried over into the next year's budget cycle. The new funding cap was now $500,000. Under new leadership, the association re-submitted the proposal, but never reduced the level of promised activities. Staff had simply assumed that project was the same as it was the previous year!

After extensive negotiations, some significant adjustments were made in the work plan and deliverables. The only thing that saved the association was that it was the only organization in the state that could fulfill the requirements of the grant. However, individual member organizations made up some of the shortfall with in-kind contributions, and the association paid the salary, fringe benefits, travel, and other expenses of the grant manager. Contracts also had to be renegotiated with subcontractors.

In the end, everyone involved deemed the grant to be a success, and the state was very pleased with the final results. Disaster was narrowly averted.

Using Unit Cost Analysis

Some RFPs require that the budget include unit cost analysis. Unit cost analysis is sometimes called true-cost analysis. There are two definitions of unit cost analysis:

Definition 1: How the total cost of the project is correlated to the impact on one person in the project.

Definition 2: The average total cost of producing one unit of output.

Let's assume that you are delivering a series of life enrichment programs to assisted living residents. If we assume that your total budget is $25,000 for 2 years and that 200 assisted living residents will benefit, your unit cost is calculated by dividing $25,000 by 200, which results in a unit cost of $125.

Since that unit cost may seem high for an enrichment program, you may want to add an explanatory paragraph like this, which includes the decreasing unit cost of the grant over time:

While the unit cost is $125 for the life of the grant, with facility-wide adaptation of this life enrichment programing, the program will serve additional people over the years. Given resident transition rates per year [use number if available], at least ___ more people will benefit over each subsequent year, for the next 3 years, making the long-range unit cost only $____ for 2 years and $__ for 5 years.

Is unit cost analysis always required in grant proposals? The answer is no. However, if you have time, it is a good idea to determine it just to see how reasonable your costs are.

What If I Overspend the Budget?

Finally, despite all our best efforts, we sometimes overspend our budget. In most cases, we overspend in some budgetary categories, say personnel, but underspend in others. If you are proactive, you can discuss this situation with the funder well before the end of the project as you are likely to be able to re-arrange the budget as long as your total costs stay the same.

It is far more problematic if you overspend in all areas. You should be aware that every funder will always place an emphasis on your budget. And, even with very good budgetary controls, you are always at risk of overspending. If this happens, expect to have to cover the costs from your own budget.

In the box below, you will find some of the common reasons for what appears to be overspending of your budget. After checking and finding that you have, in fact, overspent your budget, contact your funder as soon as possible and resolve the issue.

> ### COMMON REASONS FOR OVERSPENDING
>
> Errors in salary and fringe benefits.
> A partner fails to meet its in-kind contributions.
> Credit card purchases are not properly controlled or allocated.
> Charges may be incorrectly posted to your account.
> Charges for late payments to a supplier.

Tips:

1. Be sure that your accountant is aware of these dangers and will be diligent in working to prevent them.

2. Be sure to check with your funder to see if funds can be moved from one category to another. **Never assume that this is always the case.**

Illustrative Line-Item Budget

Before providing the line-item budget exemplar, we need to review the grant in more detail than we did for other exemplars. The Nale City Multiservice Senior Center (Nale City MSC) is seeking a grant to develop a fall-prevention program we call Stop Falls Now (SFN). SFN is a fictitious program that is representative of a number of excellent evidenced-based programs. For reasons of copyrights and permissions, we decided to use a fictitious program for this sample budget.

SFN is an evidence-based fall program developed in Sweden. SFN has been successfully used throughout Europe, the United States, Australia, and Japan to reduce the incidence of falls among older persons. Over the past 10 years, numerous studies have appeared in leading academic journals that support the effectiveness of the program.

SFN uses a train-the-trainers approach. In the United States, providers are trained over a 3-day period at one of our five training sites. Upon completion of the training course, instructors are supported by a regular webinar series to keep them up to date on the latest information as well as to improve their training skills.

Participants attend twice-weekly training sessions and are encouraged to practice the techniques of SFN on a daily basis. Older persons who complete the course often remain with the program as volunteers to help others to obtain the maximum benefits from the program.

The specific requirements of the Nale Foundation for writing the line-item budget are minimal:

> *You can use your own format for the line-item budget. Create a line for in-kind and cash matching funds. Complete a separate section for each year.*

COMBINED TWO-YEAR BUDGET: STOP FALLS NOW EVIDENCE-BASED PROGRAM (DOLLARS)			
Budget Category	**Year 1**	**Year 2**	**Total**
Salaries (2 staff @ 5% FTE)	5,000	5,200	10,200
Fringe	1,400	1,456	2,856
Advertising	1,500	1,200	2,700
Equipment	250	0	250
Supplies/training materials	1,000	1,000	2,000
Travel (to training location)	1,980	0	1,980
Training (fee for two trainers)	2,800	0	2,800
Supporting volunteers	700	500	1,200
Total direct costs	14,630	9,350	23,986
Total indirect costs (17%)	2,232	958	3,190
Total costs	16,862	10,314	27,176

INCOME AND IN-KIND (DOLLARS)			
Budget Category	**Year 1**	**Year 2**	**Total**
3% time of the $55,000 salary of the executive director, 2% increase Year 2	1,650	1,683	3,333
In-kind time of intern	500	1,500	2,000
Fall-Prevention Fiesta fundraiser	0	1,000	1,000
Total income and in-kind	2,150	4,183	6,333

Total Request = $27,176 − $6,333= $20,843

Concepts That Would Be Detailed in the Budget Narrative

Two staff: Annual salary of $50,000 each, 5% time each year with a presumed salary increase in Year 2.

Advertising costs: Recruitment of participants and volunteers and include posters, mailings, and outreach to minority groups.

Travel costs for two trainers: Regional training in the capital city including airfares and hotels.

Support costs for volunteers: Stipends for attending training, conducting workshops, and local travel.

No fee for participation: You would have to explain: Because so many participants have incomes at or slightly above the poverty line, we do not feel that they would be able to participate if they were charged a fee. After completion of the grant, we plan to offer the program to the broader community, where community members would be able to take advantage of it at a reasonable fee, which will also help with sustainability.

In-kind contributions:

- 3% of the executive director's time.

- Portion of the revenue (estimated at $1,000) generated from the "Fall-Prevention Fiesta" fundraiser that will allocated to support the project.

- Value of time of a college student doing an internship at Nale City MSC who will gather data for the evaluation and conduct the evaluation, estimated to be $2,000.

And, finally, perform the unit cost analysis: The total cost of the grant divided by number of participants over a 1-, 2-, and 5-year period. (We suggest using the extended time period to show that the unit cost goes down as the project continues.)

CHAPTER CHECKLIST

☐ Does your budget match your work plan? To make sure this happens, did you do a careful comparison?

☐ Did you bring your fiscal management team into the process of creating a budget as early as possible in writing your proposal?

☐ Does your budget cover all the costs of the proposed project?

☐ If your proposal is requesting multiyears of funding, has your budget accounted for increases due to such things as inflation and wage increases?

☐ Do your budget numbers match the amounts discussed in your budget narrative?

☐ Have you applied the principles of unit cost analysis where appropriate?

CHAPTER 13

....
··· · · · · · · ·

CORPORATE CAPABILITY AND QUALIFICATIONS

CHAPTER OVERVIEW

In this chapter, you will learn:

- The definition of a corporate capability statement

- Usual components of this section

- The importance of tailoring the corporate capability statement

- Tips for writing the corporate capability statement

- An exemplar of a corporate capability statement

Introduction: What Is Corporate Capability?

In the corporate capability section, you describe why you are able to conduct the proposed grant. Components of this section are typically taken from existing official documents and include a mission statement, the catchment area, proof of past experience in the proposed area, staff qualifications, and other related items. As always, additional items relevant to your project may be used. Also, some proposals (RFPs) may ask for additional items.

Importance of Tailoring the Corporate Capability Section

Think of the importance of the corporate capability section from the perspective of the funder, which will be deciding which entity will receive its money for a specific project: Does the funder:

> Select an applicant that only provides basic information on the organization's background and reputation but does not state why it would be great for the purpose you have in mind?

> *versus*

> Choose an applicant that provides ample information about its background and reputation, but also details relevant expertise in working on projects like the one proposed?

SHARING WHAT WE HAVE LEARNED

The most common mistake we have seen when reviewing this section of a grant proposal is not considering its marketing potential. Instead of tailoring the section to the qualifications needed to conduct the proposal, applicants sometimes simply cut and paste their mission statement, create a generic list of all the work they have done, and paste in "canned" descriptions of key staff. Nothing leaps out to the reviewers to make them think these applicants are especially strong for this specific proposal, even though they may be. Do not leave any of your assets hidden!

Here is an example: Let's assume a local Area Agency on Aging (AAA) is preparing a proposal to develop health-screening services for aging veterans in their region because the closest VA hospital is 50 miles away. They provide their mission statement, note their two years of experience with working with the local department of health on health screening, and add one-paragraph job descriptions of key staff and the amount of time each of them have worked with the agency.

This information may be adequate. However, imagine that this AAA also noted that (a) the staff included two veterans, one of whom had previous experience in working on health issues with veterans and will be the project director, and (b) that a member of the AAA advisory board is also on the board of directors of the local chapter of the Veterans of Foreign Wars and will serve as a liaison between the project and this chapter. The degree to which this AAA seems qualified and likely to be successful has just increased exponentially!

Tips for Writing This Section

1. Tailor your corporate capability section to highlight past experiences and staff skills that relate to the project. If none, stress the similarities between other work and the proposed work in the project.

2. Include the legal name of your agency, a statement of 501(c)(3) status, a sentence or two each about its history and mission (more if they are fascinating!) and catchment area, and anything else requested in the RFP. (You can lose points for omitting answers to any questions posed.)

3. List your agency awards, other accomplishments, and experience with managing grants.

4. Explain how the agency works well with other agencies that may be involved in the project.

5. Add (if the RFP permits it) letters of commitment as an attachment and reference these letters in the narrative.

6. Ask each collaborating agency to write a letter of support. Offer to provide a template letter of support that they can modify. Instruct each potential respondent to tailor their letter to show how they will benefit from the project and how well they believe your agency can lead the project. This request to tailor each letter is also important so you do not have identical letters of support, a tip-off that the applicant agency wrote them!

7. Sometimes the funder does not allow appendices. If there is room in the text, write something like, "Three community partners have written enthusiastic letters of support for this project, pledging active participation in client recruitment. These letters of support are available upon request."

8. Describe why your agency is well qualified to manage the finances of the grant. Note the background and experience of your chief financial officer and information on your last audit. (You may be required to include your last audit report.)

9. What do you do if you had a recent audit that revealed problems? Ideally, you would wait until the next audit is excellent, or at least have a plan of correction in place. If you want to apply anyway, explain how you have corrected the problem as best as you can.

10. What do you do if you have no grant experience at all? You should emphasize the skills and experience you have that relate to the proposal. Instead of saying, "We have no experience in running grants but we are eager to learn," comment on how the agency has, perhaps, worked with grants sponsored by other organizations, has had excellent outside audits, and has skills in the areas needed in the proposal.

Illustrative Corporate Capability Section

As you will remember from Chapter 5 ("Three Fictitious Organizations Serving the Aging"), The Nale City Multiservice Senior Center is seeking a grant to develop a fall-prevention program. The specific requirements of the Nale Foundation for writing the corporate capability section are:

> *In addition to a description of your agency and staff, include (a) how your organization will sustain the project*

after the funding period ends and (b) experience with managing grant projects.

Agency and Staff Description

The Nale City Multiservice Senior Center is a 501(c)(3) service center for city residents established in 1980. It is funded by the Area Agency on Aging (AAA), but is managed by an independent volunteer board. Its mission to enhance and support the *well-being of seniors in its community.* It serves as the focal point for services for more than 500 older adults from throughout the city. The center provides not only meals but also information and assistance, recreation, education, and limited transportation services. While some services require participants to pay a modest cost-share, most are free and there is no membership fee. We work closely with the three senior centers in the county. Participants are active and generally do not have major mobility or self-care issues.

In 2015, the Nale City Multiservice Senior Center won the annual Excelsior Award from the State Department of Aging for its excellence in senior programming and services. The award highlighted its informational and referral programs, its drama program, and its intergenerational local history project.

We have a stellar staff for this specific project. Most importantly, the recreational therapist has four years of experience in running exercise programs and will be the director of the proposed project. Our executive director possesses a master's degree in social work, 10 years of experience with the agency, and an additional 10 years of experience with another senior center. There is additional professional staff of three people (average tenure of six years), including a licensed nutritionist and two outreach workers, one of whom will be the second person working on the project.

Experience With Managing Grant Projects

The Nale City Multiservice Senior Center has a track record of successful grant management. We are currently in Year 3 of a grant to teach computer skills to older people, funded for $75,000 by the State Department of Education and two local computer companies. We are also operating an intergenerational local history project funded for $6,000 by the County Historical Society. In the past, we have operated five state grants in the areas of health prevention, caregiving, and telephone reassurance, ranging in size from $10,000 to $100,000. These programs are now an ongoing part of our organization and are self-sustaining. (See attachment for details.) Our fiscal operations are excellent. All projects were operated successfully with no operational or fiscal concerns. The office has had clean, professional outside audits since it began operations.

How the Agency Will Sustain the Project
We have worked hard to develop ways to sustain the fall-prevention program after funding from the Nale Foundation ends. First, once the program has been tested, we will not be incurring continued start-up or evaluation costs (other than for satisfaction surveys or staff-training costs that the agency will assume). The remaining yearly cost to offer the program two times a year will be about $7,000. This cost will be met by (a) charging a participant fee of $35, with donations covering the cost of those that cannot pay (total per year $3,000); (b) creating an annual "Fall-Prevention Fiesta" fundraiser, raising an estimated $1,000 each year for SFN; and (c) adjusting our budget to make any remaining costs up to $3,000 an annual operating expense (see letter from our board for directors.)

CHAPTER CHECKLIST

☐ Does your corporate capability section have information that is tailored to the needs of the application?

☐ Have you included sufficient documentation about your fiscal management experience?

☐ If applicable, did you to explain how your agency will work with other entities on the project?

☐ Have you included all of the specific items requested in this section of the RFP?

CHAPTER 14

....

ILLUSTRATIVE LETTER OF INTENT

CHAPTER OVERVIEW

In this chapter, you will learn about:

- The purposes of a letter of intent, also called a query letter or concept paper

- Tips on writing a letter of intent

- How to use a sample letter of intent (included here) to craft your own.

Introduction

Some funders require a letter of intent as a first step in the application process. Letters of intent are also sent by applicants to funders to see if there is interest in the proposal concept. This short chapter will cover these different uses of a letter of intent. Note that other terms for letters of intent are *query letters* and *concept papers*. For ease of reading, the term *letters of intent* is used throughout this chapter.

Definition: In all cases, a letter of intent is a short summary of the grant proposal you plan to write, containing the information you would normally include in an executive summary. It is usually in letter format on your business letterhead and addressed either to the president of the funding agency or another person identified in the application.

The Three Different Types of Letters of Intent

1. Letters of intent requested by the funder to determine how many applications they will receive.

2. Letters of intent requested by the funder as a kind of "qualifying round"; that is, all applicants send a letter of intent, but the funder invites only the applicants who had the most appealing letters of intent to submit a full proposal.

3. Letters of intent used by the applicant to see if the funder has any interest in receiving a proposal. (This type of letter of intent is the one sometimes called a query letter or concept paper.)

When a letter of intent is required by the funder, it is due well before you submit a proposal. Some funders that ask for a letter of intent consider them optional, but many do not. Be sure you know this information.

Letters of intent requested by the funder just to determine how many applications the funder will receive. When a funder requests a short letter of intent without asking for much detail, it is usually a way for the funder to anticipate how many applications it will receive and what will be the general focus of these applications. This information allows the funder to prepare for review by hiring enough reviewers and, sometimes, adding reviewers with the right expertise to rate your proposal.

A letter of intent of this kind is not rated for content. It is simply a required Step 1, and everyone who submits one will be able to later write a full proposal. Having said that, the letter of intent must be clear and not something you dash off with errors in it. It is your first contact with the funding agency, and as we have written before, first impressions count.

Letters of intent requested by the funder as a kind of "qualifying round." In this case, you are competing with other potential applicants just for a chance to submit a proposal. Staff of the funding agency or reviewers read these short letters of intent and rank them. Only a percentage (which varies widely by funders and the volume of letters of intent received) of the applicants will then be invited to submit a full proposal. Needless to say, this process requires a letter of intent that is crystal clear, compelling, and as full of information about the project as possible in the little space you are given.

There are benefits when you need to submit this kind of letter of intent. You will have written about one to three pages and will hear from the funder is if the proposal is of interest. You will not have gone to the extensive effort of submitting a full proposal that is not of interest to the funder. In turn, the funder is spared the task of reading full proposals that will not be of interest to it.

However, writing letters of intent of this kind is one of the most challenging processes in the grant application process. Why? It is challenging because you are likely to be writing this letter of intent *before* you have completed the grant, *before* your internal and external critiques are done, and *before* you are 100% sure of your best approach. Yet, you are asked to describe your proposed project in detail, albeit in miniature form, as well as make your concepts and approach appealing enough to get through an initial round. You are also expected to provide a projected budget. It is tough!

Further, note that it may be risky to vary the major elements of the letter of intent very much if you are then invited to submit a full proposal. It might not matter to the funder, but it may matter greatly, and in grant writing, chances like this are usually not worth taking. Therefore, it is ideal to be (a) working on grant concepts and (b) have the commitment of potential partners long before a grant opportunity comes along. (Haven't you heard this theme throughout this book?)

Our recommendation is to stick closely to what you proposed in the letter of intent because (a) you know the funder liked what you had written in terms of concepts and costs in the letter of intent, and (b) you do not know if changes you make will be equally liked. This recommendation does not mean that no changes can be made. Indeed, some changes will be expected between the time you write the letter of intent and the full proposal, but, in our opinion, they should be modest in nature, for example, a slight budget difference and some refinements to the general concept, not a change in the concept itself.

Letters of intent used by the applicant to see if the funder has any interest in receiving a proposal. In this case, the funder may state on its web page or literature that it prefers a letter of intent as an initial way of approaching this funder. These letters of intent are reviewed on an individual basis. Alternatively, you may find a new funder that does not welcome queries by telephone. A letter of intent may be a good way to assess interest by the funder.

If the funder suggests submitting a letter of intent but does not require one or you are thinking of providing one on your own, it is a judgment call as to whether you should submit one. Here are some pros and cons for submitting a letter of intent that is not required:

Pro: We are certainly "pro" submitting an optional letter of intent if you already have a lot of complete and well-vetted content on your proposal already completed. Here are two reasons to do so:

1. You are making it easy for the funder. That is always a plus.

2. You are not wasting your time on a full proposal that may not be of interest.

Con: Alas, there is a case for not doing an optional query letter. Here are some concerns:

1. If you are guessing on content, you may be selling yourself short with information that is not compelling.

2. The short length may make it too challenging to explain your proposal fully and the funder will not understand it and turn it down. Perhaps a full proposal would address questions better.

If, as we have suggested throughout this book, you have done pre-planning in anticipation of an application opportunity in the area addressed by the request for proposal (RFP), you should submit a letter of intent of this kind. In fact, in the letter of intent, you could add, "We have been planning a project of this kind for some time and have been seeking the right funder." Such a sentence would be both accurate and appealing.

Tips for Writing a Letter of Intent That Will Be Actively Reviewed by a Funder

1. Just as you would for writing a full proposal, follow the format exactly as requested.

2. If there is no specific format given, we suggest following the outline below, if it works for your particular proposal. Note that you usually will have one to three pages allowed. Therefore, give as much relevant detail as possible given page limits. (Easier said than done!)

The introduction. The name of your organization, location, 501(c)(3) status, the amount of funding requested, a concise description of the project and why the project is important, including overall goals and objectives. If it is not very obvious, explain how the project is related to the interests of the funder. If you have an important theme or phrase that summarizes your project well and will catch the interest of the reviewer, use it here. If you are asked to do so and have some done preliminary budget work, provide a range for your funding request. (If you are not asked to do so, it is best not to commit yourself to a budget range.)

About your organization. Write a brief description of your agency and its history and, most importantly, why your organization will excel at conducting the proposed project.

Why the project is needed. See Chapter 8 ("Developing an Effective Needs Assessment"). Summarize greatly, but include supportive data.

The evaluation and methodology. See Chapter 10 ("Evaluation and Logic Models") and Chapter 11 ("Building a Logical Work Plan (Methodology) and Timeline"). Summarize greatly, focusing on the evidence base that supports the validity of the approach you plan to take and the bare bones of the evaluation design. If there is enough room, create separate paragraphs for each.

Resources you possess. What assets not already discussed in your description of your agency do you have to succeed at the project? Include collaborators, in-kind and matching funds, and any particular staff expertise.

Closing. Express thanks for the opportunity to present this letter of intent and your willingness to answer questions, and provide contact information and your sincerest hope to be invited to provide a full proposal because the proposal is so compelling.

Note that other formats will work when no particular format is given. However, be sure to include all of the elements listed above and any others that seem appropriate for the particular proposal.

3. Think back to Chapter 3 ("Conceptualizing the Multiple Roles of a Grant Writer for Aging Services"), in which we stressed your role as a marketer. Make sure that you have used powerful action verbs and images to make this letter of intent appealing. A dry litany of facts about your proposal concept will be far less engaging than one that shows some deserved professional excitement. Having said this, do not go overboard with capitals, explanation points, and flowery language. It is a business document, after all.

4. The CEO should sign this letter, not the grant writer!

5. Use all of the proofreading and editing techniques described in Chapter 15.

Illustrative Letter of Intent

This letter of intent to a corporate funder (not the Nale Foundation) has requested a two-page (double-spaced) letter of intent. (Not all letters of intent use page limits. Many more rely on word or character counts and even specify font type and font size. Be sure that you understand requirements.)

Notes before reading the fictitious letter of intent:

1. Assume that this application will be used *instead of* an application to the Nale Foundation.

2. The bracketed notes show how this particular letter of intent is carefully drafted for a corporate funder rather than a research-oriented foundation.

3. Because this a potential funder that is very likely to have little, if any, knowledge of elder care issues, there is more explanation of culture change than there would be otherwise.

4. Use of sentences like "Documentation will be provided in a full application" works for many but nor all letters of intent. Check the requirements to be sure.

The sample letter below contains useful hints in italics about approaching a corporate foundation.

(Agency Letterhead)

Date

Name of contact person (formal letter, do not use first name)

Address of company

Dear_____:

The Many Churches Skilled Nursing and Rehabilitation Center (Many Churches) requests $15,000 to help bring care innovations to our residents, many of whom are relatives of your employees. *[Note: For applications to corporations, it is helpful to make a connection between the corporation and its products or employees.]*

Our *overall goal* is to change our residents' world to be more home-like, thereby increasing quality of life. We will create "neighborhoods" instead of hospital-like units, which will be our county's first effort toward a "culture-changed" nursing home. *Culture change* is a term used to describe a cluster of design and staffing changes that create a home-like environment in nursing homes. The concept of culture change has been studied nationally and internationally and has had impressive results. Sadly, it is not yet an option in Nale County.

The goal for the small part of the project to be funded by the ABC Corporation is one critical subset of the overall goal: to change the culture of meals in three prototype units.

Objectives for this targeted goal include (1) creating three family-style dining spaces and one kitchen for each of 12 rooms, thus creating family-style dining for 36 residents; (2) engaging these residents in preparing and planning meals; and (3) serving as a prototype for the facility-wide renovation and later as a model for other area nursing homes. *[Note: Objectives are normally far more specific than this! Because this is an application to a small, local corporation that is not focused on research and this is a letter of intent, in this particular case, the lack of specificity will do. It will not do in a formal proposal, however.]*

Many Churches is a 200-bed not-for-profit nursing home 1 mile from ABC Corporate Headquarters. *[Note: The language here makes another direct connection between the applicant and the corporation.]* It has maintained a positive reputation in the community. It has excellent state surveys and a 4-star (the highest) federal rating. *[Note: Never assume that any funder will understand the language of elder care. Therefore, the 4-star rating system is explained.]*

Why the project is needed: Research has amply shown that the kind of culture change we plan has positive effects on measures of residents' quality of life: choice, autonomy, dignity as well as staff satisfaction (documentation in full proposal). Having this kind of nursing home in our community will enhance quality of life for residents and provide increased satisfaction for staff and family members.

How the project will work: Your grant will (a) supply the materials for three large kitchen counters, kitchen supplies, and family-style dining tables for three new "household-sized" dining rooms and (b) will combine with income from other funders to complete the "culture-changed" eating experience. We will start work in May 20__ and expect it to be completed in 18 months. Staff training and family orientation are planned for a 3-month period and are also funded independently. Since this approach has been validated by numerous research projects over the past 10 years, we are not allocating valuable funds to an additional research study.

Resources for the project: Your support will enable us to complete the proposed prototype project. *[Note: It is always helpful to show that a project is almost ready to start and the contribution of the funder will make the critical difference.]* Many Churches has an ongoing, but separate, capital $__ million campaign for related physical renovations that is already at 80% of its goal at $____. Of this money on hand, 5% will provide matching funds for the cost of construction on the project proposed here. The board has separately allocated funds for stoves, sinks, and exhaust fans. One board member, a contractor, will donate the labor for the renovations. Financial and planned construction details will be provided in the full report.

In conclusion, we greatly hope you share our excitement of bringing this world-class model of nursing home care to our community and will request a full proposal in which we will provide all the critical financial and planning information that could not fit into this letter of intent. In the interim, if you have any questions, I would be pleased to answer them. Contact me at (phone and email) any time!

Sincerely,

__ (Name of CEO)

CHAPTER CHECKLIST

☐ Have you carefully reviewed the requirements (if any) for the letter of intent (due date, length, font, format, etc.)?

☐ If the letter of intent is optional, have you considered the pros and cons regarding submitting one?

☐ Have you marketed the letter of intent to conform to the funder's needs?

☐ Did you cover all of the items and questions that the funder wants included if this information is available? If not, have you included all the elements recommended in this chapter?

CHAPTER 15

TRICKS OF THE TRADE: REVIEWING
THE COMPLETED PROPOSAL

CHAPTER OVERVIEW

In this chapter, you will learn to:

- Triple-check deadlines and grant requirements

- Use prewritten modules that you will customize for each application

- Make your proposal appealing to the reviewer

- Avoid four common flaws

- Edit your narrative effectively

- Protect yourself against lost files

- Use smart strategies for (a) shortening a proposal and (b) completing online applications

Introduction

The authors have a combined experience of 60+ years of writing grants and reviewing them. We gathered the tips we have learned throughout these years and shared them with you here. Most were discussed in earlier chapters, but we felt it would be helpful to provide them again in a concise form in this review chapter. We urge you to read this chapter each time you start or review your proposal.

Tips for Developing Successful Grants

Tip 1: Triple-Check Grant Deadlines and Requirements

Before beginning your proposal, make a written list of all deadlines and requirements, and have someone else check your list. Recheck the requirements as you write. The due date is way too late to realize that you needed to double-space text and you have single-spaced the entire narrative. Similarly, you do not want to confuse "must be received by" with "must be submitted by."

It is worth repeating this warning: Be aware of the page or word limits. Grants are not consistent: Some include timelines and budgets within the page limits and some do not. Never assume you will be given a pass for longer text than permitted.

Tip 2: Use Modules

Modules are prewritten draft sections of a grant, as discussed in Chapter 2 ("Pre-Planning Your Grant Proposal: Modules and Sharing Your Grant Concept to Get Critical Feedback and Support"). In review, the purpose of modules is to free you from as much last-minute writing as possible. Sections of an application that can be drafted in advance (but not finalized) include parts of the budget, demographics to be used in a statement of need, and the corporate capability sections.

A good way to use professional volunteers and interns is to have them develop these sections in advance. For example, they can prepare a needs assessment module for a variety of programs you might want to have.

While it makes tremendous sense to prewrite sections of a grant, this recommendation comes with a caveat: **Modules must be modified to meet the needs of each particular proposal.** In Chapter 13, we discussed how to modify the corporate capability statement; all modules written in advance should be similarly modified.

Tip 3: Make Your Proposal Easy to Follow

Reviewers read many proposals, and they get tired and impatient when they have a hard time finding the information that they need. Tired and impatient are certainly not the emotions you want the reviewer to have when reading your proposal. Therefore:

- Use the sections in the application packet as subheadings— this helps the reader see where you are.

- Keep to the order of the topics as written in the grant guidelines.

- Sometimes a request for proposal (RFP) will tell you exactly what criteria will be used to judge the proposal. Be sure to address any known funding criteria, using the same wording if possible.

- In a lengthy proposal, add a table of contents (if there is room) and paginate so reviewers can easily find a section to reread.

- Write like Ernest Hemingway, not James Joyce!

- Avoid jargon and acronyms, or at least explain them.

- If there are no requirements regarding page makeup, such as margins and font sizes, use your judgment to make each page easy on the eye. Which of the following will a harried reviewer view more favorably?

A crowded text, small font, no margins at all, but with every possible detail

versus

An easy-to-read text that omits some detail but is easier on the eye

Tip 4: Avoid Four Common Flaws That Reduce Points You Could Receive

Here are four common flaws we have seen:

1. **Assuming page limits are not rigid.** They almost always are. When we do workshops, members of the audience sometimes comment that they would never submit more pages than allowed in a section or the whole narrative. They are often surprised when we tell them that, as reviewers, we know that this happens, and it happens more frequently than one would think. Do not count on an online application template providing a message that you have exceeded the page or word limit. Most do, but that is not always the case.

2. **Ignoring specific guidelines in the request for proposal (RFP).** For example, in the needs section, don't describe only a national or state need when you were clearly asked to describe a local need.

3. **Providing lazy answers.** For example, an RFP contains the question, "How will you ensure that elders of all ethnic groups will participate?" A lazy answer is, "We will engage elders of all ethnic groups to participate in our project" with no further detail. This response simply turns the question into a sentence and does not answer it. You do not earn points by this kind of lazy statement.

    A more adequate answer would be something like this: We plan a tri-pronged approach to engaging elders of all ethnic groups in our project. We will (1) market the project in the six houses of worship for minority groups in our catchment area, (2) include leaders of all local ethnic groups in our community (African American, African, Latino/a, and Asian/Pacific Islanders) on our steering committee and follow their suggestions for recruitment, and (3) work closely with two English as a second language (ESL) programs serving all of ethnic groups (see letters of support).

4. **Having numerical or other discrepancies.**

Example 1: The executive summary states that 100 clients will be served, the narrative says 150, and the budget allows for only 80. As a result, the reviewer cannot determine the cost–benefit of the project and begins to suspect that the applicant is either careless or confused.

Example 2: One project manager is included in the methodology section, but the budget has costs for two managers, and there is no mention of the second manager being paid with in-kind funds. As a result, staffing levels and costs are unclear, leaving the unpleasant perception that the budget is being padded.

Tip 5: Edit Your Narrative Effectively

No exceptions to this rule: Have someone edit the proposal who has not been engaged in writing it. No writer catches errors in his/her own work as well as an outside objective person does. Sloppy writing with numerous errors in spelling or punctuation creates a negative impression. Also, a phrase that is crystal clear to you may be mystifying to someone else.

Tip 6: Ensure Consistency

Use the **Find and Replace** feature in your word processing program to be sure that numbers, project names, and so forth, remain consistent as your project evolves. For example, after completing the budget, if you find that you will be able to engage only 80 elders instead of the 100 originally planned for your project, search the narrative for "100." Then, look at each occurrence and change the incorrect number 100 to 80 as appropriate. (It is important to check each occurrence, as you may want to keep the number 100 in sentences not relating to the number of elders.)

Tip 7: Never Make "Spell-Check" Your Final Proofing Activity

Reproof after spell-checking to be sure that a spell-check disaster has not occurred. An embarrassing truth: One of us almost submitted a final report to a funder in which the word "inconvenient" was spell-corrected to "incontinent"!

Tip 8: Protect Yourself Against Lost Files

Even if your computer has a reliable back-up system, it is prudent to place copies onto a flash drive that is kept separately from your computer. Alternatively, send draft iterations to a colleague by email attachment, with a request to hold these drafts for you until the grant application is submitted. You can also send copies to yourself for cloud storage. With this approach, someone will be able to access your work even if your computer crashes or is lost, or you cannot get into the office.

Tip 9: Shorten Your Proposal If Necessary

Proposals often grow beyond the number of pages, words, or characters allotted to them. Most writers, ourselves included, find it challenging to omit text already written. We tend to feel that every single sentence is critical. It may help to remember that all applicants (not just you) have the same space limitations, and all are also probably cutting material they would like to keep. Here are some tips we have used for paring down text:

- Have someone else you trust and who knows your agency go over your text. Accept their deletions, as hard as it may be!

- Instead of using five citations to document a fact, use one citation, like this: Five diverse sources (list them) concluded that a lack of socialization is a health risk for elders living alone.

- See if you are allowed to simply put the author and date of citations in the text and list the full citations separately in a references section or endnotes.

- Avoid passive voice. It takes up more space than active voice.

- Use short, declarative sentences.

- Turn lists into paragraphs.

- Instead of providing subsections with a heading title with a space underneath, consider bolding a subsection name. Follow it with a colon and run the text on the same line. If, as is sometimes the case with online applications, you cannot use boldface, use capital letters. (This is a last resort and should be used only if all other options fail, as it makes the page crowded and harder to read.)

• Do triage. If your text is still too long, look at your lists and bullets. Omit the least important and also any accompanying text related to what you have omitted.

Tip 10: Use These Strategies for Online Applications

Write your proposal on your computer instead of writing the text directly on the online application form. This process allows you to share with colleagues and edit more efficiently. However, early on in the writing process, input your working draft into the online form. Compare the word or character count showing on your computer and that of the online application. For some reason, we have often found that the counts do not match, and when this happens, there always seems to be a higher count showing on the online application and hence less room for all of your text. Similarly, when a section is nearly done, put it in the online form to check for word count. You do not want to find that your proposal's length is wrong on the day you are submitting the application.

Sometimes you cannot see the next section of an online application until you have finished the first section. This can be problematic if you want a good overview of the requirements for the additional sections. If this happens, simply type in any text and move on to see the next section. Needless to say, be sure to erase the text you entered for this purpose.

Last, if you can, print out the final version of what you have inputted into the online application. It will let you see spacing errors and check that each section has been entered into the correct space.

Tip 11: Stay Calm During the Day the Application Is Due

Somehow, someway, your application will be submitted on time!

CHAPTER CHECKLIST

☐ Triple-check for grant deadlines and requirements.

☐ Use prewritten modules, remembering to modify as needed.

☐ Make your proposal easy to follow for the reviewer.

☐ Avoid the four common flaws that reduce points you could receive.

☐ Check closely for numerical and other discrepancies.

☐ Edit your narrative effectively.

☐ Protect yourself against lost files.

☐ Shorten your proposal using the tips in this chapter.

☐ Remember that there are differences between traditional and online submissions.

☐ Stay calm! You will get your application in on time.

PART IV

FINDING AND UNDERSTANDING
FUNDING SOURCES AND PROCESSES
TO FOLLOW POSTFUNDING

CHAPTER 16

·······························

FINDING AND WORKING WITH FUNDERS

CHAPTER OVERVIEW

In this chapter, you will learn about:

- Types of funders

- Sources for finding out about funders

- Looking for support from grant makers not normally focused on aging

- Two funding tips for governmentally funded agencies in aging

- What to do if you are a for-profit entity?

- Approaching funders

Introduction

We deliberately chose to place this chapter toward the end of the book. We believe that you should first know what grants your organization needs and make sure that it has the capacity to manage these grants well, and then—*and only then*—focus your attention on getting funded. Indiscriminate grant chasing is not a good use of an agency's time.

However, let's be realistic: Sometimes you will find in your email or someone will bring you the most perfect request for proposal (RFP) for your organization but with a very short deadline. Of course, you will probably choose to reply. If you do, be sure you can guard against the possible implications of a rushed application (incorrectly budgeted, planning errors, giving a poor impression of the agency to the funder). Also, never skip internal and external critiques, even if they are in very truncated form. Keep in mind that sometimes it is better to give even a great grant opportunity a pass rather than submit a slap-dash one.

A sad fact: Finding potential funders is particularly challenging for aging service providers. Despite the rapid "graying" of America, foundation sources for funding for aging programs are hard to find: In a 2011 report, the most recent available at the time of writing, the Foundation Center revealed that only 2–4% of all grants awarded were to agencies serving the aging (from the Foundation Center's IssueLab website: http://foundation-center.org/gainknowledge/research/pdf/fgt11highlights.pdf).

Why there is such a disheartening disconnect between funding and demographic imperatives is a good question, but it is the reality that agencies in aging must face. Therefore, this chapter contains not only the expected overview of types of grants and where to look for grants for aging services, but also specific strategies for seeking funding from sources that do not traditionally fund aging services.

Types of Funders

There are three common types of funders for all kinds of grants:

- Governmental (local, state, federal)
- Private foundations (large, small, regional)
- Corporate foundations

Governmental Grants

Governmental grants are mostly given at the federal and state level. Large counties and cities may also offer grant funding. These grants usually require the most complex, most evidence-based, and longest proposals. Therefore, such grants are not ideal for a novice grant writer. We recommend that if you are new to grant writing and are determined to apply for a large, complex governmental grant, you should contract with someone familiar with the federal or state grant-writing world to work with you. It is also common to be rejected for a large governmental grant and then make revisions and be funded the second or even third time.

Governmental entities usually call for a request for application (RFA), which typically requests proposals for a defined research topic or program and tells the applicant exactly what the objectives of the research or project will be. Put another way, governmental grants usually have a set result in mind and are looking for applicants who can produce those results. However, governmental funders sometimes use program announcements, which are somewhat more open-ended.

Resources for federal grants that fund in aging are commonly found for free at various governmental websites. Among these are the following:

- Grants.gov: http://www.grants.gov/ (Use the pull-down menu to refine the list to the areas you seek.)

- Administration on Aging (part of the Administration on Community Living, under the U.S. Department of Health and Human Services): http://www.aoa.gov/ (Click on funding opportunities.)

- Corporation of National and Community Service: http://www.nationalservice.gov/build-your-capacity/grants/funding-opportunities

Some members of Congress and some elected state representatives provide their constituents, upon request, with information about federal or state funding options. It is worth making an inquiry to find out. Most states also offer online resources to search for grants and/or send out emails about funding opportunities. The best way to find them is to look at the state's departments of health and aging websites.

Foundation Grants

A foundation grant comes from a nongovernmental entity that is established as a nonprofit corporation or a charitable trust. The purpose of a foundation is to award grants to unrelated organizations, institutions, or individuals for scientific, educational, cultural, religious, or other charitable purposes. (See the Grantspace website: http://grantspace.org/tools/knowledge-base/Funding-Resources/Foundations/what-is-a-foundation.)

Generally, foundations use a request for proposal (RFP), which may generally define the area in which they are interested, but welcome different approaches from the applicant. For example, they may specify that they want to fund programs to help elders live independently at home, but will expect to receive diverse approaches and, in fact, may welcome an unusual approach if there are some reasons to expect that it will be successful. In other words, while some foundations will want an evidence base to show that a project is likely to be successful, others are willing to be more on the cutting edge and experiment with new ideas. The guidelines of the foundation will help you determine what is expected.

Foundation grants vary widely in size and scope. Some award large-scale grants, while some may award extremely modest ones. Some foundations require an application process that is as rigorous as the largest federal grants.

Community foundations are in most cities, counties, and large towns. Commonly, they are an entity in which individual donors pool their donations so that a professional team can invest their money and award grants on their behalf. Search for them in your community by googling your area and the words "community foundations." In general, awards tend to be small, but they are a great place for a beginner to start.

Family foundations are established by individual families. Many give only to preselected organizations within a family's personal interest.

Learn more at the National Center for Family Philanthropy, at https://www.ncfp.org/serve/family-foundations, and by searching the Foundation Center's extensive array of information (see the "Foundation Center" subsection below).

Family and community foundations may have a shorter application process, which is appropriate for beginners. Depending on their charter, they can be national, statewide, or local in scope. Some community and family foundations will even limit their funding to a particular city or part of a county.

Corporate grants are (surprise!) grants awarded to a not-for-profit by a corporation. Sometimes corporate grants seek to support projects that meet their marketing or public relations needs. By marketing needs, we mean they are interested in grants that (a) might sell their product and (b) create a positive image of their corporation, locally if small or nationally if large. Typically, however, corporate grants have predefined areas of interest, which you can find by searching the resources listed above or simply googling the corporate name with the word "foundation."

Local corporate grants are common and often are made only in areas in which the corporation has a physical presence. Banks, for example, often provide small community grants. Sometimes corporations do not provide cash, but rather in-kind donations, such as their employees' time or product donations.

In Chapter 14 ("Letters of Intent"), the exemplar is a letter of intent to a corporate funder. Bracketed notes provide guidance on how to craft an approach to a corporate funder.

The Foundation Center. An ideal way to learn more about foundation and corporate grants is to make use of the generous online information provided by the Foundation Center. We suggest that you make use of their free webinars or tutorials such as those found on the following sites:

- http://grantspace.org/training/courses/introduction-to-finding-grants

- http://grantspace.org/tools/knowledge-base/Funding-Re-sources/Foundations/what-is-a-foundation

- http://grantspace.org/training/courses/introduction-to-corporate-giving

There are many other resources (free or paid) on the Foundation Center's website that are also worth exploring, including the free newsletter, at http://foundationcenter.org/newsletters/.

Tip: Consider using interns, board members, or volunteers to help you with the search.

Sources for Finding Out About Specific Grant Makers That Are Appropriate for Your Project

One of the most traditional ways to find potential funders is to travel in person to your local Foundation Center, housed primarily in the libraries of bigger cities. You can find the Foundation Center Library nearest you by going to http://foundationcenter.org/fin/. A dated approach, surely, in these days of "click and read," but it gives you access to databases you might otherwise miss or have to purchase.

You will be surprised at how many funders are listed when you look at the databases. Note, however, that many state that their grants are "limited to preselected organizations." Do not bother approaching them unless you know someone on their board who may be able to add the name of your agency to their list.

There also are multiple fee-for-service websites that alert you to grant funding. The one we have personally used and liked is found at Grant-Watch.com (http://www.grantwatch.com/). This does not mean others may not serve you better. You can find a review of others at The NonProfit Times (http://www.thenonprofittimes.com/news-articles/finding-grants-through-online-databases/).

Another option: Look at the annual reports of other agencies serving older adults and see what funders have supported them. You can then research these funders and see if your own project would fit into their priorities. Keep in mind that requesting a grant for a project similar to one that they have just funded in your own community is not likely to be successful. It is also a disservice to the community. It is best to use this approach to find funders, not to copy projects.

Looking for Funding From Funders That Do Not Normally Support Aging Services

In the beginning of this chapter, we noted that few funders specifically have a focus on supporting grants in aging. One possible way around this limitation that we have used is to "reframe" the way you present your proposal so it can be brought to funders that would not usually fund a proposal on aging services.

Two examples in which each of us obtained a grant in aging from funding sources that had not one word about aging in their RFPs:

1. Federal Department of Education: One of the authors (Carol Hegeman) was looking for grants to get more volunteers in nursing homes. The initial rationale for the grant was the shortage of direct care staff, a topic hardly the purview of an education department. However, the more we thought about it, the more it seemed to us that recruiting needed to begin by promoting a positive view of working with the elderly. We realized that to develop a vibrant system of elder care, we needed more people to understand the positive work done in aging services.

   Accordingly, by working with a consortium of colleges, the agency developed a proposal to test the feasibility of having a student service-learning program in elder care. As part of this service-learning experience, students would volunteer in a variety of nursing homes and then participate in a service-learning course focused on elder care. This proposal not only met the needs of the funder ("innovations in higher education") but also served the aging community. Incidentally, this grant led to (a) 10 years of related funding in service learning in elder care programs and (b) the college textbook *Elder Care and Service Learning* (Seperson & Hegeman, 2002).

2. The Institute of Museum and Library Services, based in Washington, DC: The other author (William Lane) worked on a project designed to improve the quality of visits by family members in nursing homes. The partners on the grant were a university center on aging, three county-sponsored nursing homes, a county Area Agency on Aging (AAA), and a nationally recognized museum. The museum was the lead agency (the agency that applied for and managed the grant). "Cultural kits" were created, using objects, historical photographs of the region, and photos of Hudson River School paintings from the museum's collection. The cultural kits were used by families as conversation starters when they visited relatives who suffered from Alzheimer's disease and were living in one of the three nursing homes.

Here are some ways to "reframe" projects serving the aging so they might be funded by a funder not normally engaged in the aging field. For example, you can submit:

- Exercise programs to funders in wellness and health
- Intergenerational programs to funders in youth
- Outdoor improvement grants for a nursing home and indoor projects to reduce energy use to environmental funders

Three Funding Tips for Governmentally Funded Agencies in Aging
Many foundations and corporations limit their grants to 501(c)(3) not-for-profit entities. This limitation, of course, leaves many Area Agencies on Aging (AAAs) and their related programs, which are sponsored by local governments as well as other governmental entities, looking only to funds from the state or federal sources. There are three other options these entities should consider:

1. Forming a not-for-profit subsidiary that can be used to apply for foundation and corporate grants that may exclude governmental agencies from applying. Once you have this subsidiary in place, you can use it to apply for foundation grants. Forming

a not-for-profit subsidiary requires a series of steps and legal support. States generally provide assistance to government-sponsored AAAs and other groups to help them create such not-for-profits.

2. Forming a collaboration with a not-for-profit community partner in which the community partner will apply for a grant and you will be one of agencies working along with the community partner. While this approach will not always work, since some foundations will not allow governmental agencies to benefit from their grants at all, it is worth exploring.

3. Forming a collaboration with a university or college. This option makes the most sense if you are already planning to use academics to conduct your evaluation.

In all of the above cases, the agency loses leadership of the project as the applicant is considered the lead agency. This also means that indirect costs are awarded to the applicant. However, if an agency cannot apply on its own, it may be an acceptable alternative.

What to do if you are a for-profit entity?

In short, not much. On rare occasions, some funders, especially government agencies, will allow for-profit entities with special expertise to apply. If you are a for-profit, our suggestion is that you partner with a not-for-profit that can apply as the lead agency. Check the grant guidelines as sometimes for-profit entities cannot participate in any way.

Another approach is applicable for consultants who have their own business: Share an idea with a not-for-profit and see if they will hire you as independent contractor to work on the project.

Approaching funders

When we do our grant-training workshops, we are often asked, "Should we call up a funder to ask about our proposed application and whether or not it is a good fit?" Alas, the answer to this question is, "It depends."

If the RFP provides a program officer's name and invites questions, of course, go ahead and make your call. However, with this very first telephone call, you are providing someone who may be managing the review of your application with a first impression of your organization. Therefore, you need to sound organized and professional by (a) having specific questions about one or possibly two proposed projects and (b) planning the call well so all of your preliminary questions can be answered at this one time.

One way to be able to repeat a call is to ask, "May I call again?" and get a positive response. Make any additional calls judiciously so as not to wear out your welcome.

A note here: We have found program officers to be extremely helpful and friendly. Keep in mind, however, that they are not usually the ultimate decision makers. It is wonderful to know that a program officer approves of or even loves your concept, but that is not a sign that you will be funded.

If the RFP states "No further information will be given," do not call! A funder is likely to think that if an agency cannot follow a direct request on an RFP, they are unlikely to be trusted to follow other guidelines.

If the RFP is silent on calls, whether to make a call becomes a decision on your end. What we have done in this situation is to call and ask if a call for more information will be welcomed, and then we take it from there.

An indirect way to find out more about an entity that takes this approach (i.e., no guidance on calls) is to look at its annual report to see what other grants were like. For governmental grants, you can also use the Freedom of Information Law (FOIL) to see what a successful application looks like.

FOIL requests are not free and sometimes require a formal and complex application process. It is only worth the effort for a major large-scale grant. You need to know the exact name and of the funded project and often the federal ID number of the grant, which can be found by searching for recent grants funded by the agency.

FOIL requirements (sometimes called FOIA, for Freedom of Information Act) vary by state and by governmental agency, and you may have to search FOIL requirements for the grant program you want on line. For information on the federal Administration on Aging (AoA), for example, follow this link: http://www.acl.gov/site_utilities/FOIA/info_guidelines.aspx. For each FOIL request, be sure to include your name and contact information in the cover email.

One final point: If a funder offers a bidding conference (an opportunity to hear about the RFP and perhaps to pose questions), be there at all costs. You will learn as much from the questions other people pose as you will from answers to your own questions.

In summary, it requires a lot of time and effort to find the funders who are appropriate for your project. However, taking the time to find the ones who are most likely to support your project in the long run is less time-intensive than submitting proposals to funders who have minimal or no interest in funding you. Search well!

CHAPTER CHECKLIST

☐ Are you clear on the differences and usual requirements of different types of funders?

☐ Are you availing yourself of the various online resources to find out about grant opportunities?

☐ Are you checking annual reports of organizations similar to your organization?

☐ Have you considered "reframing" a grant concept so it might appeal to a funder not usually focused on aging?

☐ For governmental entities without a 501(c)(3), have you considered working with a lead agency that is a 501(c)(3) to prepare the application?

☐ Are you clear on the ways to approach a funder by telephone?

CHAPTER 17

··

PROCESSES TO FOLLOW POSTFUNDING

CHAPTER OVERVIEW

In this chapter, you will learn:

- The five steps in the postfunding phase

- The major grant management tasks

- What to do about the protection of human subjects

- Audits by the funder

- The basics of progress reports

- Overspending your budget

- Carry-over funds and no-cost extensions

- Closing out your grant

Introduction

Success! Your award letter of acceptance has arrived, and you have been funded. When the letter arrives, everyone is thrilled. Your CEO is delighted and news releases are prepared. You take some time, as you should, to celebrate. But suddenly everyone, and especially the principal investigator (PI), realizes that with this terrific news comes a whole set of new responsibilities—you have a grant to implement, manage, and complete successfully.

One caveat: As with evaluation, the management of grants is both a broad topic and a specialized topic. Entire books have been written on the subject (see Ward, 2009). Even the topic of the financial management of grants (see Daniels, 2015) is covered in specialized books. This chapter is meant to be a very basic guide.

Grant management is both an art and a science. Your agency is now responsible for carrying out the goals and objectives set forth in the proposal using the funds in the way they were specified in the budget. In order to manage your grant successfully, you will find that the more time you spend paying attention to the details, the more likely you are to have a successful grant. Where does the art come in? You need also to be able to think creatively: How can you overcome the unforeseen obstacles that will occur? How can you win over that one staff member who is interfering with the project?

First Steps in Funding Phase

Now that your celebration is over and the realization of your responsibilities has set in, you have so much to do in addition to actually starting and implementing the grant. While the funder will provide you with technical support so that you can meet the terms and conditions of grant, the bulk of the work is now up to you. Here are some critical steps:

Negotiation

First, review the Notice of Award to make sure it matches your proposal. There may be a surprise. While it is the hope of every grant writer that his or her proposal will be accepted unconditionally by the funder, it does not always happen. As a general rule, the larger the grant, the more likely that the funder will require changes in your funded proposal. You may be asked to modify your methodology or make some changes to your budget. The funder may want you to do some things you had not counted on in developing the proposal, such as coming up with a plan to include more minority elders in your project, making some changes in your work plan, or reducing the costs by 10–50%. The thing to remember is that negotiation is normal and does not reflect on the quality of your proposal. After all, you were funded!

Organize and Verify

You should address any concerns the funder has in writing and make sure that the funder also agrees, in writing, that all their concerns have been satisfied once you have incorporated them into the revised proposal.

Start Project Files

We recommend at least five project files: (1) all the information about the award and correspondence with the funder; (2) all your budget information along with expenditures; (3) project information, including minutes from meetings, records of phone calls, and copies of any marketing materials; (4) evaluation materials; and (5) insight or consumer feedback on the project for future replication and to include as content in the final report.

Most projects run from 1 to 3 years. If you have trouble remembering what you did last week, think about what you will be facing at the end of your project, when you will be trying to complete your final report and document things that you did months ago. Keep updating these files in a timely and ongoing basis so that later you will have everything you might need to complete your final report. Further, in case you are suddenly offered a new job, you will leave your replacement with good, solid information.

Plan on How You Will Document Your Project

With smart phones it is easy to take photos and email them to yourself to insert later into a file. But, if you are organizing events, doing construction, or conducting programs, you may want to have someone with an actual camera take digital photos for you. This is a great job for a volunteer who is interested in photography. Be sure to keep copies of articles that appear in the media and any publicity generated about the project. Also, you don't have to wait until the end of the project to do satisfaction surveys. Find out how you are doing as the project progresses. In all your publicity, be sure to include any wording about the funder that the funder has requested.

Announce the Award to the Community

Your grant award is a valuable public relations opportunity. Let the public know that you have received this grant and what you intend to accomplish. Once all the negotiations have been completed and you are ready to move forward, don't forget to announce the award to the community. Whether you are going to do such things as offer classes to help prevent older people from falling, work to improve the communication between staff and clients, or improve the lives of nursing home residents, you are increasing the capacity of your organization to serve the needs of older people living in your community. If you receive a state or federal award, your elected representatives should be acknowledged and thanked as well.

Also, from this very first announcement onward, you should take every opportunity to acknowledge and thank your funder. Even if they do not request this acknowledgment, and some do, it helps you build a relationship with your funder for future support. Of course, first check with your funder to be sure this publicity is welcome and if there is particular wording they would like to see in any publicity.

Management Tasks

There are numerous grant management tasks. Some are tasks are general and apply to almost all grants regardless of the funder. It is these general tasks that we discuss here. The scope and content of each of these management tasks will depend on a number of factors, including the size of your award, the length of the award period and the funding course. For example, if you receive a large, multiyear award from a federal source (e.g., the National Institutes of Health), you can expect to have site visits throughout the duration of your project. On the other hand, a smaller grant from a community foundation may or may not involve site visits and will likely have much less rigorous compliance requirements.

The following list is not in sequential order, but the activities will all need attention at the same time:

1. Step up your budget management procedures. As soon as you receive your award notice, you need to begin to work with your accountant(s) to set up the necessary budget controls. First and foremost, there should be no comingling of grant funds with those of your agency.

2. You need to make sure that your accountant is using standard accounting procedures to monitor and report the use of all funds and to document clearly that awarded monies are being used only for the funded project. At one time, it was standard practice to open a separate checking account for a new grant. Given the new on-line banking options and inexpensive checking accounts, you may still want to use this option. Always check with your program officer for any specific requirements they might have regarding financial record management and reporting.

3. Get all your required institutional paperwork in place. If you are part of college or university, there will almost certainly be an office in your institution with a title such as grant management, sponsored research, or institutional advancement. In most cases, you cannot submit a grant without going through this office, and the people there will guide you through much of the post-award activities. If you are not working in an educational institution but are collaborating with an academic one, you may be asked to work with, and conform to, some of the regulations set forth by the institution. Larger health care organizations, as well as nursing home and assisted living chains, also have such grant management offices.

If your agency is a freestanding aging service agency, you need to create and manage this paperwork, both online and in print. Set up files from the beginning and add new ones as you need them.

Make sure that more than one person is familiar with using these files and knows how to add to them and access them.

4. Hiring and orienting new personnel, if necessary, can be time consuming. One of your first tasks will be to start working with your human resources or personnel department to initiate the hiring process. Ideally, you have at least some guidance in the proposal in terms of job descriptions for your new hires as well as for those existing staff members who will become part of your project team. While recruitment and interviewing can take considerable time, you want to make sure that you hire the right staff the first time. Staff turnover on a grant can be both disruptive and a drain on your budget.

As for orientation (now often called *onboarding*), be sure that your new hires have more than a general knowledge of the facility, know how to interact with others in your organization, and how to work as a team. Be sure they understand the reasons the agency wrote the grant, the funder expectations, and any relationships with other people and entities engaged in the grant. As appropriate, bring them to as many planning meetings as possible.

5. Create the necessary subcontracts and memoranda of understanding (MOUs). As soon as possible, you will want to put subcontracts with consultants and other grant participants in place. In some cases, formal subcontracts (which usually are enforceable in court) may not be necessary, but you will need to initiate an MOU, which usually is an unenforceable agreement. It is wise to consult with your attorney as you write any kind of agreement.

6. Review your work plan and/or timeline as soon as possible. If you see any glaring changes or errors, they may need to be approved by your funder.

7. Call a staff meeting. Bring all your existing staff together and go over all aspects of the grant activities. You will also want to establish a regular project staff meeting schedule. Depending on

the size and scope of the project, at least some of your staff will be taking on grant activities as part of their jobs. Also, most of your consultants and subcontractors will not be full-time on your project. So, set meeting times that fit with everyone's calendars. You may want to tie reimbursement to outside contractors not only to their performance but also to their attendance at these meetings.

8. Don't forget your project partners. As soon as you are funded, inform your partner organizations of the good news. Along with an MOU or contract you may be creating with them, make sure they receive a copy of the award and the proposal to make sure they understand both their roles and responsibilities. Some of these partners will be your subcontractors. But, in any case, you want to make sure they understand (a) the funding and payment schedules, (b) all reports that are required along with due dates, (c) the services they are to provide, and (d) the consequences if they do not meet their obligations. We have found it wise to go over all of these issues in person if possible, even when working with a partner who is only going be involved in one portion of the grant, for example the start-up phase. Keep them informed about the progress of all phases of the grant.

Protection of Human Subjects and Clinical Trials

If you are conducting a randomized clinical trial, you are now are required to register your project with the federal Protocol Registration and Results System. To register, go to ClinicalTrials.gov at https://register.clinicaltrials.gov/. The registry will inform the public of your clinical trial, which is necessary if you want to publish your findings and also acts as another form of the protection for the human subjects.

For other types of projects with human subjects, you may need to gain approval from what is known as an institutional review board (IRB). IRB review is only required if your project meets the federal definition of research: The Federal Policy for the Protection of Human Subjects (Common

Rule) defines research as "a systematic investigation, including research development, testing and evaluation, designed to develop or contribute to generalizable knowledge" (http://www.hhs.gov/ohrp/regulations-and-policy/regulations/45-cfr-46/index.html). It is here that you will find detailed information on informed consent.

Obviously, this is a very broad definition of research. When you look at this site, you will see exemptions such as, but not certainly limited to, many education and training programs.

However, be sure to explore this site to determine whether or not you need to gain approval from an IRB.

This area is another example of when using an academic researcher can be helpful. Further, you may want to consider working a local college or university to gain IRB approval. Almost every educational institution has an ongoing IRB approval process in place. For additional guidance consult the Department of Health and Human Services web address in the preceding paragraph. Note that is always best to err on the side of caution in the area of IRB requirements.

Ongoing Management Issues

Audits by Your Funder

If you receive a grant from a community foundation, you will probably not have any ongoing audits beyond the monthly, quarterly, or yearly reports it will require you to submit. This may not be true for grants received from larger foundations and/or governmental agencies. Many larger foundations will require an independent audit. If you receive a large, nonfederal grant, you can probably expect a visit at some point during the process by an audit team. What kinds of things will they be looking for? Selected examples are:

> **1. Internal financial controls.** Universities and larger service delivery organizations usually have some type of "sponsored research office" that will provide technical assistance and training for the project director and other staff. If you are at a smaller agency that is receiving a large grant you will need to work with your

funder from the outset to ensure that you understand your sponsor's requirements and fiscal requirements. If you are very new to managing a grant, do not hesitate to seek help to get your financial controls in place. You may have a knowledgeable board member, or the funder itself may be able to provide training or at least make suggestions for assistance.

2. Performance outcomes. Oversight and regular reporting on your progress in meeting the short-, mid-, and long-term objectives of your project as set forth in your work plan and/or timeline is standard practice. Your funder wants you to be successful, so they may will be willing to work with you to ensure compliance with the goals and objectives you put forward in your proposal.

3. Time commitments of personnel involved. Every grant budget contains time commitments for personnel, both at your agency and your partner organizations. If you state that your PI, who is also your director of clinical services, will devote 0.4 FTE (full-time equivalent) to the project, you are stating that this person will be spending 40% of his or her work time on the project. This time must be documented online or on paper and approved by the project director. The same rules apply to all personnel who have been listed in your budget as contributing some portion of their time to the grant. Work with your payroll department to make sure that your participant records are accurate and properly documented.

As noted in Chapter 12, be sure that no one is charging more than 100% of his or her time on any activity. For example, a project exercise trainer cannot work 60% on ongoing exercise programs, 30% on your grant on fall prevention, and 25% on another grant supporting a walking program.

If you are working on a federally funded grant, you will be subject to the regulations set forth in the 2013 White House Office of Management and Budget (OMB) *Uniform Administrative Requirements, Cost Principles, and Audit Requirements for Federal Awards* (commonly called "Uniform

Guidance") (OMB Uniform Guidance, 2014), which sets the audit requirements. In most cases today, the new regulations stipulate a single audit for federal grants of more than $750,000. Most agencies now must submit a single audit reporting package to the federal Audit Clearinghouse. If you are applying for a new grant that will increase the total of all of your federal grants to more than $750,000, you should add an appropriate share of the cost of this audit to your budget.

If you have received a large, multiyear federal grant, you will probably receive a site visit from the funding agency. If you are new to this process, it may seem as if a small army has invaded your office. Depending on the size and scope of your award, your visiting team may include federal program staff, federal grant management staff, and technical assistance consultants. You will be required to have all your financial management systems up to date. Other records that they may want to review are personnel and human resources (HR) policies and procedures, subcontracts, and related records; all your procurement policies and procedures; and your administrative controls. For complete information, consult the Health Resources and Services Administration (HRSA) website at http://www.hrsa.gov/grants/manage/index.html.

The bad news: All audit reporting and regulations are difficult to understand. The good news is that most federal agencies will provide you with very good support in all phases of your project. All the federal agency grants management documents, including OMB Circulars, can be downloaded at https://www.whitehouse.gov/omb/circulars_default.

The most important thing to remember is that careful pre-award planning leads to fewer post-award problems. Many of the problems that can occur in the post-award phase can be reduced by careful planning during the proposal-writing (pre-award) phase. Be sure that you are developing your proposal in such a way that it meets the audit and compliance requirements of your potential funder. Make sure that everyone, from your CEO through all of your partners and potential subcontractors, understand what they will be required by the funder to do if you receive the award.

Progress Reports

Every federal agency and foundation will monitor your progress throughout the grant by requiring that you use a very specific set of directions and instructions. For example, the National Institutes of Health (NIH) requires that progress reports be submitted using PHS 2590 forms (https://grants.nih.gov/grants/funding/2590/2590_forms.pdf). All funders, including NIH, generally require some progress reporting. While the topics and amount of detail vary greatly from funder to funder, most funders will either require or suggest that you include the following seven common areas in your progress reports:

1. **Budget and financial updates.** This is always at the top of every list. You will need to explain where you stand in terms of income (in-kind contributions, fees, etc.), expenditures by all specific line items, and fund balances remaining. The subject of overspending will be discussed below.

2. **Program progress.** This is an update in terms of what you promised to do in your proposal and what you have actually accomplished. This should be tied to your work plan or timeline.

3. **Program outcomes.** While evaluation activities are usually geared toward the final report, interim reports should also bring the funder up to date in terms of evaluation activities and findings.

4. **Changes that have been necessary.** This is where you report minor changes, for example, using a YMCA instead of a senior center to hold a scheduled activity. If this change does not require any changes to the budget or the types of clients served, it will just need to be included in the update. However, if the change is something major, especially if it requires changes to your budget, call or request a meeting with your funder to get prior approval.

5. **What have you learned to date?** This can be an important section in your report. What challenges have you encountered? What successes have you achieved to date? Are there lessons that

you have learned that might be helpful for other organizations like yours to know and that would also be useful information for the funder in its future grant-awarding activities?

6. Attachments. Don't forget to attach some of those photos you have been taking, the publicity you have generated, copies of newspapers articles (not just your news releases), and copies of any materials (brochures, flyers, etc.) that you have produced since your last report. But, don't overdo it—be selective!

7. Remember your partner organizations. Be sure to include what your partners have been doing (or not doing) to support the grant. Make sure they get full credit for what they are doing.

All of the above topics will be also generally be covered in your final project report.

What If I Overspend the Budget?

This topic was discussed in Chapter 12. Be aware that every funder will always place an emphasis on your budget. And even with very good budgetary controls, you are always at risk of overspending. Your accountant should be aware of these dangers, and be sure to check with your funder to see if funds can be moved from one category to another.

Carry-Over Funds and No-Cost Extensions
Carry-over funds. If you have a multiyear grant, you may well face the issue of carry-over funds, meaning that instead of overspending, you have not used up your budget for the year. The question then becomes, for example, if I only spend 80% my budget during the first year, may I carry over those unspent funds into the second year? The answer is—it depends.

Most foundations will permit you to carry over funds from one year to the next if you can, in writing and with support, justify this action. In most cases, you will need to submit a revised budget showing (a) your original budget, (b) unspent funds in each budget category, and (c) a revised second-year budget. There are many reasons for having unspent funds. For example, you estimated consulting costs at $10,000, but you overestimated these expenses by $2,000. All the work was completed, but that $2,000 remains, and you would like to carry it over and use it in the next year.

No-cost extensions. If at the end of your grant period, you have unspent funds and tasks left to perform, it may be possible to receive a no-cost extension from your funder in order to complete all the goals and objectives of your grant. The general requirement is that you will need to write a letter at least 30 days prior to the end date of the grant, but requirements vary and cost extensions are not always possible.

The letter should clearly state the tasks remaining, the amount of money left to carry over, the length of time of the requested extension, and, most importantly, the documented reasons for your request. If you have been keeping in close contact with your funder, they should not be surprised by your request. The most common reason for a no-cost extension is a mismatch between your official starting date and the date you actually received the money.

A note for those of you who are working a federal grant: The federal government has created what is known as expanded authority, which allows some recipients to carry over funds without gaining prior permission. If you receive a federally funded grant and have been granted expanded authority privileges, it will appear in the remarks section of your award notice. The following actions are covered by expanded authority: Carry over of up to 25% and onetime cost extension. More detail can be researched if you are in this category.

Closing Out Your Grant

Congratulations are again in order. You have completed your project, and the quality of life and/or care has been improved for the older people you serve.

If you have received a small award ($25,000 or under), your final report may be the first formal written report you make to the funder. All other interim reports will simply have been verbal reports to a project officer. Many foundations now require that you submit this final report online. In addition to documenting how the funds were spent, most funders will want to know (a) what the grant accomplished, (b) what challenges you faced and what you learned, and (c) how you will sustain your project without continued grant funds.

For larger and more extensive grants from foundations, the same type of information will be required, along with other topics. In preparing your final reports for these larger grants, you will have your progress reports to work from.

The closeout steps for a federal grant are found in OMB Uniform Guidance (2014). According to this document, you must submit "all financial, performance, and other reports required under the grant within 90 days after the grant award expires or is terminated." The original awarding entity will review these reports to ensure compliance with all the grant terms and conditions of your grant. They will also focus on ensuring that all your funds were spent properly.

Until the foundation or federal agency confirms that your project is finished, you are still responsible for complying with and fulfilling all the terms of the grant. The closeout period, even for small grants, can take several months.

Important: Most federal agencies, as well as other funders, will require you to retain all of your grant records for 3 years from the date of the final closeout.

Beyond Your Final Report—Dissemination of Your Findings

Now that your grant is completed, you will want to consider how you are going to let the world, or at least your community, know about what you have accomplished. Planning for this process, which is formally known as dissemination, should begin shortly after you start your grant. Here are some venues to consider:

1. Presenting at a regional, statewide, or national conference.

2. Putting your final report on your website and using social media.

3. Publishing your findings in a research journal (this will be more likely if you are partnering with a college or university).

4. Making presentations to local groups. This is the one that most of us overlook. In some cases, these types of presentations (to a long term care coalition, Rotary Club, etc.) may be more important to some of your local partners.

5. Submitting press releases to local, statewide, or national media as appropriate.

6. Adding a tag line to all of the agency's letterheads, brochures, web pages, and other publications about the project.

7. Printing a story in your annual report. (One of us had such a story picked up by a national newsletter.)

8. Invite reporters, stakeholders, and government officials to a debriefing section at the end of a project.

All of these activities will be important when you apply for your next grant. You will want to let your next prospective funder know that not only did you achieve the goals and objectives of your project, but also that you shared your results with the appropriate scientific and professional groups as well as your local community.

Reminder: As we have stated elsewhere, this book is a guide to general grant writing and not advice on how to manage a specific grant. It is critical that you study and follow the specific guidelines your funder provides, as there may be differences and additional requirements from what is written here.

CHAPTER CHECKLIST

☐ Have you settled all pending issues with your funder before starting the project?

☐ Have you set up a project file and planned how you will document your project?

☐ Have you announced your award to the community?

☐ Are all your management procedures, paperwork, personnel, and subcontracts ready?

☐ Have you reviewed your work plan and/or timeline and set up scheduled staff meetings?

☐ Do you have IRB approval (if necessary)?

☐ Are you prepared for any required audits by the funder?

☐ Have you set the necessary procedures to complete any required progress reports?

☐ Do you have the necessary controls in place to prevent overspending your budget?

☐ Have you considered how you will disseminate your findings?

REFERENCES

Albert, S. M., & Logsdon, R. G. (Eds.). (2000). *Assessing quality of life in Alzheimer's disease.* New York, NY: Springer.

Boutaugh, M. L., Jenkins, S. M., Kulinski, K. P., Lorig, K. R. Ory, M. G., & Smith, N. L. (2015). *Generations, 38*(4),107–118.

Brody, E. M., Dempsey, N., & Pruchno, R.A. (1990). Mental health of sons and daughters of the institutionalized aged. *The Gerontologist, 30*(2), 212–219.

Brownie, S., & Nancarrow, S., (2013). Effects of person-centered care on residents and staff in aged-care facilities: A systematic review. *Clinical Inventions in Aging, 8,* 1–10.

Campbell, D. T., & Stanley, J. C. (1963). *Experimental and quasi-experimental designs for research.* Chicago, IL: Rand McNally.

Cassie, K. M., & Cassie, W. E. (2012). Organizational and individual conditions associated with depressive symptoms among nursing home residents over time. *The Gerontologist, 52*(6), 812–821.

Centers for Disease Control and Prevention. (2011). *Family Caregiving: The Facts.* Retrieved from http://www.cdc.gov/aging/caregiving/facts.htm

Clark, H., & Anderson, A. A. (2004, November). *Theories of change and logic models: Telling them apart.* Paper presented at the annual meeting of the American Evaluation Association, Atlanta, GA.

Cohen-Mansfield, J., Ejaz, F. K., & Werner, P. (Eds.). (2000). *Satisfaction surveys in long term care.* New York, NY: Springer.

Cox, N. (2002). *National Study of Adult Day Services, 2002–2002 (CD).* Princeton, NJ: Robert Wood Johnson Foundation Partners in Care. Retrieved from http://www.rwjf.org/pr/product.jsp?id=20940

Daniels, M. L. (2015). *Grant management non-profit fund accounting.* North Charleston, SC: CreateSpace Independent Publishing Platform.

Doran, G. T. (1981). There's a S.M.A.R.T. way to write management's goals and objectives. *Management Review, 70*(11), 33–36.

Findley, R. (2003). Interventions to reduce social isolation amongst older people: Where is the evidence? *Ageing and Society, 23,* 647–658.

Frumkin, P. (1999). Evaluating for success and the five dimensions of philanthropic impact. *Philanthropy,* Sept/Oct, 9–12.

Grabowski, D. C., O'Malley, A. J., Afrendulis, C. C., Caudry, D. J., Elliot, A., & Zimmerman, S. (2014). Culture change and nursing home quality of care. *The Gerontologist, 54,* 535–545.

Gozalo, P., Parkash, S., Qato, D. M., Sloane, P. D., & Mor, V. (2014). Effect of the bathing without a battle training intervention on bathing-associated physical and verbal outcomes in nursing home residents with dementia: A randomized crossover diffusion study. *Journal of the American Geriatrics Society, 62,* 797–804.

Hegeman, C. (2003). Peer mentoring of CNAs in nursing homes. In A. Weiner & J. Ronch (Eds.), *Culture change in long term care* (pp. 183–196). New York, NY: Routledge.

Jamison, D. T, Breman, J. G., Measham, A. R., Alleyne, G., Cleason, M., Evans, ... Musgrove, P. (Eds.). (2006). *Priorities in health.* Washington, DC: The World Bank, International Bank for Reconstruction and Development.

Kaufman, R., & Guerra-Lopez, I. (2013). *Needs assessment for organizational success.* Alexandria, VA: ASTD Press.

Kim, H., Chang, M., Rose, K., & Kim, S. (2011). Predictors of caregiver burden in caregivers of individuals with dementia. *Journal of Advanced Nursing, 68*(4), 846–855.

Krueger, R. A., & Casey, M. A. (2014). *Focus groups: A practical guide to applied research* (5th ed.). Thousand Oaks, CA: SAGE.

Koenig, M. (2014). *Don't start your nonprofit grant writing until you read this.* Retrieved from http://www.nonprofithub.org/grant-writing/when-to-start-nonprofit-grant-writing/

McCormick, K., & Salcedo, J. (2015). *SPSS statistics for dummies* (3rd ed.). Hoboken, NJ: Wiley.

McKillip, J. (1987). *Need analysis: Tools for the human services and education.* Newbury Park, CA: SAGE.

OMB Uniform Guidance. (2014). Uniform Administrative Requirements, Cost Principles, and Audit Requirements for Federal Awards (commonly called "Uniform Guidance"), OMB Circular A-133 (OMB Uniform Grants Guidance §200.343). Retrieved from http://www.grants.gov/web/grants/learn-grants/grant-policies/omb-uniform-guidance-2014.html

Ortman, J. M. Selloff, V. A., & Hogan, H. (2014). *An aging nation: The older population in the United States* (P25-1140). Washington DC: U.S. Department of Commerce, U.S. Census Bureau.

Pearlin, L. I., Mullan, J. T., Semple, S. J., & Skaff, M. M. (1990). Caregiving and the stress process: An overview of concepts and their measures. *The Gerontologist, 30*(4), 583–594.

Pillemer, K., & Hudson, B. (1993). A model abuse prevention program for nursing assistants. *The Gerontologist, 33*(1), 128–131.

Pillemer, K., & Suitor, J. J. (2002). Does peer support help family caregivers? Results from a randomized, controlled experiment. *Research on Aging, 24*(2), 171–193.

Pioneer Network. (2015). *Promising practices in dining: Dignified Dining Tools and Resources.* Retrieved from http://www.pioneernetwork.net/Providers/Dining/DiningTools/

Pruchno, R.A., & Kleban, M. H. (1993). Caring for an institutionalized parent: The role of coping strategies. *Psychology and Aging, 8*(1), 18–25.

Radar, J., Barrick, A. L., Hoeffer, B., Sloane, P. D., McKenzie, D. Talerico, K., & Glover, J. U. (2006). The bathing of older adults with dementia: Easing the unnecessarily unpleasant aspects of assisted bathing. *American Journal of Nursing, 106*(4), 40–28.

Rea, L. M., & Parker, R. A. (2014). *Designing and conducting survey research: A comprehensive guide* (4th ed.). San Francisco, CA: Jossey-Bass.

Robison, J., & Pillemer, K. (2007). Job satisfaction and intention to quit among nursing home nursing staff: Do special care units make a difference? *Journal of Applied Gerontology, 26(1),* 1–18.

Roulston, K. (2010). *Reflective interviewing: A guide to theory and practice.* Thousand Oaks, CA: SAGE.

Seperson, S. B., & Hegeman, C. (Eds.). (2002). *Service learning in elder care.* Westport, CT: Auburn House.

Shara, R., Siders, R. A., & Dannifer, D. (2011). Culture change in long term care: Participatory action research and the role of the resident. *The Gerontologist, 51,* 212–225.

Sternberg, R. J., & Dobson, D. M. (1987). Resolving interpersonal conflicts: An analysis of stylistic consistency. *Journal of Personality and Social Psychology, 54*(4), 794–812.

United Way of America. (1996). *Measuring program outcomes: A practical approach.* Alexandria, VA: Author.

Ward, D. L. (2009). *Effective grants management.* Burlington, MA: Jones & Bartlett Learning.

Wolcott, H. F. (2008). *Writing up qualitative research* (3rd ed.). Thousand Oaks, CA: SAGE.

Yaffee, K., Fox, P., Necomer, R., Sands, L., Lindquist, K., Dane, K., & Covinsky, K. (2002). Patient and caregiver characteristics and nursing home placement in patients with dementia. *Journal of the American Medical Association, 287*(16), 2090–2097.

GLOSSARY

A GRANT WRITER'S VOCABULARY

abstract. A short, objective summary of a grant proposal. It is usually less than one page or may be as brief as one short paragraph.

boilerplate. Materials, information, and documents that can be stored and retrieved for use when needed in preparing proposals.

budget narrative. A section that explains the costs that are outlined in a budget, where the costs are derived from, the unit cost for services, and any in-kind and/or matching funds that will be provided.

carry-over funds. Funds that may be spent in the year following their original placement in the budget of multiyear awards. In a multiyear grant, funds allocated for a given year may not be expended as anticipated. If the investigators can justify the reasons for the need to carry over these unspent funds to the next budget year, many foundations will allow this budgetary practice.

comparison group. See *control group.*

control group. Sometimes it is called the *comparison group.* In an experimental or quasi-experimental design, the control group is the one where the participants do not receive the intervention. In aging projects directly involving human subjects, the interventions are generally some form of educational or training program.

corporate capability. Corporate capability refers to components such as an agency's mission statement, catchment area, and proof of past experience demonstrating why and how it is qualified to complete the proposed tasks and worthy of funding.

deliverables. The tasks and products that will be completed at the end of the grant.

direct costs. Expenses that can be directly assigned to the project for which an agency is seeking funding. Examples include such things as personnel costs, fringe benefits, photocopying, and supplies. These are things that will be consumed during the course of the project.

501(c)(3). Section 501(c)(3) is the portion of the U.S. Internal Revenue Code that allows for federal tax exemption of nonprofit organizations, specifically those that are considered public charities, private foundations, or private operating foundations. Almost all granters require an applicant to have a 501(c)(3) designation. In order for a corporation or other qualifying entity to receive 501(c)(3) status, it must apply to the IRS for recognition by filing Form 1023 (or Form 1023-EZ), Application for Recognition of Tax Exemption.

evaluation. The section of the grant where an agency outlines how it will both explain the process for monitoring and evaluate the success of the project in terms of achieving the goals and objects outlined in the proposal.

evidence-based. Refers to empirical research to support either the need for a program or, more often, that the program to be implemented has empirical support.

executive summary. A longer, more detailed version of the *abstract*, often running one to five pages, depending on the length of the proposal.

experimental designs. Projects that are conducted in a laboratory or highly controlled setting. The participants are drawn from one pool of subjects and randomly assigned to take part in the project as members of either a treatment/intervention group or a control/comparison group. Most aging- and human-services projects occur outside of such a highly controlled environment.

external evaluation. An evaluation conducted by an outside consultant.

formative evaluation. An evaluation type that looks only at how well the grant was conducted. This type of evaluation assesses how well the project accomplished the specific tasks outlined in the proposal.

foundation. A nongovernmental entity that has been established as a nonprofit corporation or a charitable trust. Foundations include private foundations and public charities, and their principal purpose is to make grants to unrelated organizations, institutions, or individuals for scientific, educational, cultural, religious, or other charitable purposes.

indirect costs. Indirect costs are also known as *overhead costs.* The two terms are generally used interchangeably. These are costs that are needed to complete the project, such as telephone and utilities, but exist whether or not the project is funded. However, all these costs will increase due to the increase in activity that will result from the receipt of the grant funding.

informed consent. A formal procedure to ensure that all the participants are made aware of the potential costs and risks of taking part in your project.

in-kind funds. Funds that are not actually paid in cash but are donations of services, equipment, physical space, or products to the project. Note that all in-kind funds must be documented because there is a cost associated with them.

institutional review board (IRB). An IRB is a committee created to review and approve research involving human subjects. It is in place to ensure that all such research will be conducted in accordance with federal, institutional, and ethical guidelines. Only those projects that meet the

Federal Policy for the Protection of Human Subjects (Common Rule) need to use the IRB process.

internal evaluation. See *evaluation.*

intervention group. See *treatment group.*

letter of intent. A short summary of the anticipated grant proposal. It contains the information you would normally include in the main points found in an *executive summary*. A letter of intent may be used by an agency as a form of inquiry to see if a funder has a potential interest in the proposed project. It may also be used by the funder to estimate how many completed proposals the funder might receive or as part of a *qualifying round*.

letter of support. Letter from a partner or others confirming that the organization has the necessary collaborative and community support to carry out the proposed grant activities.

logic model. A visual depiction that describes what your proposal is all about and what it will accomplish. They are sometimes called outcome models as they are designed to graphically depict the components of a proposal and clarify inputs, activities, and outcomes.

matching funds. These are funds that cover some of project costs and are donated by the principal organization, by partners, or by donors. Most governmental grants do not allow matching funds from another governmental agency. All matching funds must be documented because there is a cost associated with them.

methodology. This is a term usually found in more research-oriented grants to refer to the *work plan*. In this section of a grant application, the organization outlines how, when, and with whom they will work to complete the goals and objectives of the proposal.

modules. Prewritten sections of a proposal that, with strategic modifications, may be placed in proposals to save time.

memorandum of understanding (MOU). An MOU is a formal agreement between two or more agencies or organizations. In grant writing, MOUs are used to establish official partnerships. MOUs are not legally binding but do carry a degree of seriousness and are stronger than a gentlemen's agreement.

needs assessment. A carefully researched and factual description of the problem that grant funds will resolve. In some requests for proposals (RFPs), this section is referred to as the *rationale*. These two terms are often used interchangeably.

990 finder. This resource of the Foundation Center gives you free access to nearly 3 million of the most recent Forms 990 and 990-PF filed by nonprofit organizations with Internal Revenue Service (IRS). At the end of this form is information on grants that were awarded.

no-cost extension. An agreement to allow an agency when, through no fault of its own, it will not be able to complete the grant on time. In this case, the funder is allowing additional time to complete the grant without providing the awardee with any additional funds.

number rubric. A brief subsection of a proposal where the grantee describes the demographic and other important characteristics of the target population the proposal is designed to serve.

objectives. Measurable statements of what outcomes an organization expects to achieve by meeting the goals of the proposed project.

one-group pre- and posttest design. A research design in which a pretest is given to the group (to create baseline data). This group is exposed to some treatment, a posttest is conducted, and data are again collected. The original baseline and posttest findings are compared to see if any changes have occurred.

one-shot case studies. A research design in which a single group is studied only once. From a research perspective, this is weakest research design.

opportunity costs. Benefits that could have been gained from an alternative or other use of the same resource(s).

organizational capability statement. A description of the agency, staff, their experience with managing grants, and how the organization will sustain the project after the funding period ends.

overhead costs. See *indirect costs.*

planning abstract. A short summary of a proposal that can be circulated to gain feedback from others, including staff and management as well as potential outside stakeholders.

pretest. Data gathered in advance or preliminary testing or trial.

posttest. A test given to subjects after completion of a treatment or intervention program to measure changes that may have occurred.

progress reports. Periodic reports required by every federal agency and most foundations so that they may monitor the progress of the project throughout the grant period. The schedule and content of these reports will vary from funder to funder.

program officer. An employee of the funding entity who works with grant applicants.

qualifying round. Procedure whereby the funder reviews letters of intent in order to reduce the number of full applicants. The funder accepts only a small percentage of applicants that will then be invited to submit a full proposal.

qualitative data. Nonnumeric data that must be analyzed and/or interpreted. Such data are generally gathered through such methods as direct observations, focus groups, interviews, and surveys using open-ended questions.

quantitative data. Anything that can be expressed in a number. This type of data is usually gathered from sources such census data, existing client records, fixed-choice (such as true/false) questions, and satisfaction and consumer surveys.

quasi-experimental designs. Research designs in which the participants may or may not be drawn from the same pool of subjects and are assigned, but not randomly, to take part in the project as members of either a treatment/intervention group or a control/comparison group. Most aging- and human-services projects that involve comparing groups of participants fall into the quasi-experimental design category.

rationale. A term that is used in some requests for proposals (RFPs) to refer to the needs assessment section.

request for application (RFA). A type of solicitation notice in which a funder announces that grant funding is available. Researchers and organizations are allowed to present bids on how they think the funding could best be used. In some cases, the funder will issue a formal request for proposal (RFP) based on the results of the RFA. However, in many cases funders will request that a respondent submit a proposal based on the ideas they put forward in their initial RFA response.

request for proposal (RFP). A solicitation, often made through a bidding process, by a foundation or governmental entity. When such an entity issues a new contract for an ongoing program or a new initiative, it sends out an RFP to all qualified agencies, organizations, and service providers to participate in the bidding process.

reviewer. A staff member or contracted person assigned to read grant applications and provide objective ratings, which will be used by the funder as a major factor in its decision to fund or not fund a proposal.

statistical two-group comparison. A research design in which one group (called the control or comparison group) does not receive a treatment or participate in the program, while another group (called the treatment or intervention group) receives the treatment or participates in the program. Data are gathered on both groups before the treatment has begun and after the treatment has been administered, and the findings are compared.

statement of need. A section of the proposal that documents why a project is needed. It is sometimes referred to as the *rationale* section.

summative evaluation. An evaluation type that looks at the impact of the process activities of the project. That is, did the project obtain or did it not obtain the results intended as set forth in the objectives?

theory of change model. A model developed to link the activities and outcomes of your project and describe how they are expected to develop. Often confused with *logic models*, theory of change models not only convey the purpose and direction of a project but also show the relationships between the multiple factors that will have an influence on the outcomes.

threat. A term used in evaluation to describe factors in a project design that might make the findings questionable.

timeline. A sequential table covering all of the tasks outlined in the *work plan*. Timelines are required for most but not all grants.

treatment group. Also referred to as an *intervention group*. In an experimental or quasi-experimental design, the treatment group is the one where group members receive a treatment or intervention. In aging research, such treatments are generally some form of educational or training program.

unit cost analysis. How (1) the total cost of the project correlates with the impact on one person in the project or (2) the average total cost of producing one unit of output.

work plan. A section of a proposal that explains in detail how an agency will carry out the projected project. It is a blueprint of how the project will operate. In more research-oriented grants, this section may be referred to as the *methodology* section.

ABOUT THE AUTHORS

....

Carol Hegeman, MS, was, for over 30 years, the Director of Research at the Foundation for Long Term Care (FLTC) in Albany, NY. In that position, she successfully wrote and successfully managed numerous funded demonstration and research grants that benefited elder care providers and the people they serve. Five of these grants received state or national awards. Carol received the American Society on Aging's 2008 Gloria Cavanaugh Education & Training Award.

William C. Lane, PhD, is emeritus faculty member of the State University of New York (SUNY) Cortland and the founding Director of the Center for Aging and Human Services. He is the owner of the gerontological consulting firm William Lane Associates. Bill is a past president of both the State Society on Aging of New York (SSA) and Sigma Phi Omega National Honor Society in Gerontology. He is a recipient of the Walter M. Beattie, Jr Award from SSA.

Both authors are reviewers of governmental grants and the book shares valuable knowledge gained from that review experience.